BLUEPRINTS

Health Education Key Stage 1 Teacher's Resource Book

John Lloyd

Ron Morton

Stanley Thornes (Publishers) Ltd

BLUEPRINTS – HOW TO GET MORE INFORMATION

The following titles are currently available. New titles are being added every year.

Topics
Assemblies
Writing
Science Key Stage 1 Teacher's Resource Book
Science Key Stage 1 Pupils' Copymasters
Science Key Stage 2 Teacher's Resource Book
Science Key Stage 2 Pupils' Copymasters
English Key Stage 1 Teacher's Resource Book
English Key Stage 1 Pupils' Copymasters
English Key Stage 2 Teacher's Resource Book
English Key Stage 2 Pupils' Copymasters
History Key Stage 1 Teacher's Resource Book
History Key Stage 1 Pupils' Copymasters
History Key Stage 2 Teacher's Resource Book
History Key Stage 2 Pupils' Copymasters
Environmental Education Key Stage 1
Environmental Education Key Stage 2

Geography Key Stage 1 Teacher's Resource Book
Geography Key Stage 1 Pupils' Copymasters
Geography Key Stage 2 Teacher's Resource Book
Geography Key Stage 2 Pupils' Copymasters
Technology Key Stage 1
Technology Key Stage 2
Health Education Key Stage 1 Teacher's Resource Book
Health Education Key Stage 1 Pupils' Copymasters
Health Education Key Stage 2 Teacher's Resource Book
Health Education Key Stage 2 Pupils' Copymasters
Maths Key Stage 1 Teacher's Resource Book
Maths Key Stage 1 Pupils' Copymasters
Maths Key Stage 2 Teacher's Resource Book
Maths Key Stage 2 Pupils' Copymasters

Books may be bought by credit card over the telephone and information obtained on (0242) 228888.
Alternatively, photocopy and return this FREEPOST form for further information.

Photocopiable

Please send further information on BLUEPRINTS to:

Name _____

Address_____

_____

_____

Postcode_____

To: Marketing Services Dept., Stanley Thornes Publishers, FREEPOST (GR 782), Cheltenham, Glos. GL53 1BR

First published in 1992 by:
Stanley Thornes (Publishers) Ltd
Old Station Drive
Leckhampton
CHELTENHAM GL53 0DN

A catalogue record for this book is available from the British Library.

ISBN 0–7487–1473–1

Typeset by Tech-Set, Gateshead, Tyne & Wear
Printed and bound in Great Britain at The Bath Press, Avon

CONTENTS

INTRODUCTION

Health education in the primary school

It has long been recognised that schools and teachers have a unique opportunity in the community for helping to create a healthy environment and that health education is the responsibility of all teachers (Pamphlet 31, 1956). In acknowledging that patterns of health and education for health begin at home, Pamphlet 31 and, more recently, HMI recommend that schools should:

> support and promote attitudes, practices and understanding conducive to good health ... and that a school's regard for health education should be expressed not only through its normal academic and pastoral arrangements, but also through the whole school environment, the patterns of relationships established, the values transmitted by the personal example of teachers and other adults working in the school, and the self esteem fostered among its pupils (HMI, 1986).

The 1988 Education Reform Act makes this an entitlement for all pupils between the ages of five and sixteen, and all schools are now required by law to provide a broad and balanced curriculum which 'promotes the spiritual, moral, mental and physical development of pupils and prepares them for the opportunities, responsibilities and experiences of adult life'. The National Curriculum Council has, therefore, advised schools that 'the personal and social development of pupils is a major aim of education and that personal and social education is the means by which the aim will be achieved' (NCC, 1990a). As a **cross curricular theme** within the Personal and Social Dimension of the whole curriculum, Donahue (1991) notes, schools must give pupils health education which:

- offers them opportunities to achieve their physical, psychological and social potential;
- helps them to know themselves better and to think well of themselves;
- provides health-related knowledge and helps pupils to develop understanding and skills to use it;
- promotes positive attitudes towards equal opportunity and life in a multi-cultural society by dealing sensitively with values and with cultural and religious beliefs (NCC, 1990a).

This is very much in keeping with the European Community Resolution on Education and Health (EC, 1988) which recommends that:

- the daily life of the school should in a general way encourage a health promoting style of teaching, of learning, of human relationships, of eating habits etc.;
- the whole of the subjects taught should implicitly contribute to the acquisition of health promoting attitudes and knowledge;

- in certain thematic areas health education should form a specific part of that curriculum.

The curriculum

The biological basis for health education is apparent in the statutory curriculum for Science, AT2 (DES, 1991). However, it is important to recognise that to teach health education without reference to the appropriate Programmes of Study could reduce such work to topics in isolation, never addressing attitudes, values and the necessary skills required for making healthy choices. As a **cross curricular theme** within the National Curriculum, health education has a vital role to play in emphasising the most appropriate teaching and learning approaches in the classroom. Such approaches are fundamental to good personal and social education. Indeed, the Programmes of Study assume great importance in the development of health education given that the statutory Science curriculum makes explicit reference to health only in the Programmes of Study although, clearly, such work will remain compulsory for all pupils between the ages of five and sixteen (DES, 1991).

Teaching and learning

Teaching and learning approaches are central to the success of health education at each Key Stage. HMI (1989) consider that worthwhile learning approaches have features in common for pupils of all ages and that:

- they should be encouraged to take some responsibility for their own learning, developing self-confidence and judgement and from the earliest age, are encouraged to exercise informed choice;
- they understand that everyone's contribution, including their own, deserves attention and are able to talk about, present and display their work in a supportive context;
- they should have the opportunity to work in groups which differ in size and purpose, as well as on their own, experience leadership as well as membership of such groups, offer and respond to ideas, argue a case and defend sensibly a decision or course of action, present personal and group ideas, and take some responsibility for the outcomes of group activity.

Most importantly, HMI further consider that:

- opportunities should be created for pupils to achieve ... and that teachers ensure that genuine achievement is recognised and rewarded.

iv

Starting points

It is more than apparent from research undertaken by the Health Education Authority's Primary Schools Health Education Project (Williams, Wetton and Moon, 1989) that children have a far greater knowledge of health at an earlier age than previously thought. They also have strong attitudes and opinions about what 'makes and keeps them healthy'. It is very important, therefore, to build upon this from an early age, developing the spiral curriculum in the context of existing knowledge, beliefs and attitudes in order for health education to be effective. Moreover, it is important that such work is not undermined by the school's hidden curriculum. As the National Curriculum Council (1990b) recommends and Donahue (1991) notes, 'health messages will have a more significant impact if they are supported by opportunities to exercise skills learned in the classroom'.

Assessment

Assessment that values and recognises what it is the children have done or completed successfully is imperative. Self-assessment can be an important part of this process giving learners the opportunity to reflect, as individuals or in groups, on what they have learned, achieved or completed well, the process being practical and learner-centred rather than being teacher orientated (Lloyd, 1990).

Clearly, any process used should be about raising pupils' self-esteem and not about reinforcing failure. Consequently a variety of approaches to the assessment of individual pupil achievement will need to be practised by teachers, who will undoubtedly take the opportunity to assess simultaneously pupil performance in the 'core and foundation' subjects of the National Curriculum as well as the knowledge and understanding appropriate to the promotion of good health. However, teachers themselves will have to exercise caution in judging the performance of individual children in terms of the attitudes, values and behaviours apparent as their own will undoubtedly have a major influence on this process.

The health promoting school

Above all else, children and young people need to acquire the ability to make healthy choices and to contribute to the development of a healthy population; the restriction of choice, however well intentioned, is more about doing something on behalf of children than enabling or empowering them to take more control of their own lives (Lloyd, 1991).

Health education is about enabling children to be increasingly responsible for their own lives. But for health education to be a meaningful activity it must relate to the *whole* school curriculum and to its ethos. Teachers do need to ensure that what is taught in the classroom is supported by the often subtle messages that pupils receive about health from the school environment and the hidden curriculum. The danger is that work on nutrition, for example, can be contradicted by a school meals' service that offers little in the way of 'healthy' food choices. Similarly, work on dental hygiene may be contradicted by the sale of sweets and biscuits in the tuck shop and, of greatest concern, work on the dangers associated with tobacco use can be undermined by those adults in the school who are seen smoking. As Curriculum Guidance 5 (NCC, 1990b) comments, 'Standards, attitudes and patterns of behaviour can convey powerful messages and their significance is often underestimated'.

The notion of the school as a 'health promoting' institution is therefore very important. It should not only recognise the school environment, the curriculum, teaching and learning strategies, but also take account of and acknowledge the role of the family, the community, and the role of health professionals who come into contact with children in the school. The diagram on page viii, *The health promoting school*, sets out these and other contexts in more detail. This may be used as a springboard for INSET and whole school development, setting an agenda for further discussion and the identification of appropriate strategies for action. For this reason you will also find the diagram in photocopiable form in the Pupils' Copymaster Book so that copies can be enlarged and run off on A3 paper for whole school development sessions. *Blueprints Health Education Key Stage 1* seeks to ensure that such work is not dealt with superficially or simply 'bolted on' but has an integral place within the school and the curriculum. This approach is essential if children's entitlement to good health is to be met.

HOW TO USE THIS BOOK

What is *Blueprints Health Education Key Stage 1?*
Blueprints Health Education is a practical and comprehensive resource specifically written to fulfil all the National Curriculum requirements for the teaching of health education in primary schools. At each key stage there is a teacher's resource book and a pupils' copymaster book. The resources for the primary key stages together provide a complete and coherent curriculum spiral for health education, although the two key stages may of course be used separately.

Blueprints Health Education Key Stage 1 consists of this Teacher's Resource Book and the accompanying Pupil's Copymaster Book which contains 96 related photocopiable activities. Both the teacher's book and the book containing the pupil worksheets are written as a child-centred, active learning resource encouraging the development of pupil participation across a range of skills and activities and utilising materials that are accessible to all classrooms.

Blueprints Health Education Key Stage 1 has been written to enable every teacher to fulfil all the learning objectives within the nine areas of study for health education at Key Stage 1 as set out in Curriculum Guidance 5: Health Education. It provides nine topics, developed at a higher level at Key Stage 2, which correspond exactly to these nine areas of study in Curriculum Guidance 5 as follows:

Curriculum Guidance 5 *Learning Objectives*	Blueprints Health Education *Topics*
• Substance use and misuse	• Medicines and drugs
• Sex education	• Growing up
• Family life education	• Families
• Safety	• Being safe
• Health-related exercise	• Exercising
• Food and nutrition	• Healthy eating
• Personal hygiene	• Keeping clean
• Environmental aspects of health education	• The environment
• Psychological aspects of health education	• Feeling good

You will find the exact wording of the National Curriculum learning objectives reproduced at the start of each topic.

These topic titles have been chosen to present the content of the learning objectives in a friendly form for primary aged children.

The structure of each topic follows the same form and enables teachers easily to fit health education into their other classroom work. Because of its clearly cross curricular nature you will find a cross curricular topic 'wall' or **Building block** opening each unit: this is a diagrammatic way of showing how the topic is developed across the whole curriculum. You will then find a short **Introduction** to the topic, and the specific **Curriculum Guidance 5 learning objectives** are reproduced in an at-a-glance form. These are followed by **Starting points**, a series of awareness-raising exercises, and **Activities** related to the specific health component (e.g. 'Family life') but focusing in turn on each of the core and foundation subjects of the National Curriculum, initially stating and then addressing the actual and potential relevant Attainment Targets.

At the end of each topic various **Assessment** activities are suggested which have been designed to involve teachers, pupils, and sometimes parents. Users of *Blueprints Health Education* will note that these assessment activities are different from all the others: the purpose of this is so that the user will have at hand a range of exemplar assessment means that they can build into a repertoire of their own for pupil assessment.

Throughout the text reference is made to the pupils' copymasters contained in the companion book, however it is not essential to have the Pupils' Copymaster Book to make sense of the activities in this book. The Teacher's Resource Book can be used quite satisfactorily on its own as a core resource for health education. Where relevant, cross-referencing is also made to other books in the *Blueprints* series.

There are numerous ways in which *Blueprints Health Education* can be used. It is available for the busy classroom teacher who wishes to take from the texts whatever is required to support a particular point she/he is making in relation to some aspect of health education. On the other hand *Blueprints Health Education* can be used as a complete and systematic school resource aimed at developing and maintaining a whole school approach to the teaching and promotion of health education.

What clearly emerges from *Blueprints Health Education* is the strong personal and social model of health education upon which it is based. Children are asked to share their experiences and express their opinions and feelings on a range of matters and issues from medicines and drugs to feeling safe. Consequently, the resource is a strong medium for developing personal and social education which arguably can have significant effects not only for the raising of the self-esteem of the child but also in their performance and achievements in school. The authors are themselves practitioners working daily alongside teachers and children. It is their experience and belief that schools share concern about determining a caring school ethos and that schools regard their pastoral system as being every bit as important as their academic. It is with the support of these views in mind that *Blueprints Health Education* has been written.

The Education Reform Act (1988) and subsequent legislation, continues to promote the involvement of parents in their child's learning. Health education addresses areas of concern shared by the school and parents alike regarding the well-being of their children. Wherever possible *Blueprints Health Education* has sought to include the family and home in the pupil activities, acknowledging their importance as an overriding influence and strong resource, thereby bringing children, parents and teachers together in partnership in the learning process.

Each topic can be studied as a cross curricular topic on its own. Equally so, a teacher can decide that she/he would like to focus on a history topic with a health perspective and therefore use the history dimensions of each component within *Blueprints Health Education*. Similarly, this can apply to a topic focus on science and health, PE and health, or any of the other core and foundation subjects or RE.

By now few teachers will need reminding that there is much to be gained in integrating the curriculum into key topic areas. Key Stages 1 and 2 expect a great deal of the class teacher who has the task of providing a broad and balanced curriculum but whose major concern is to ensure that depth, often the key to genuine understanding, is not undermined by breadth. *Blueprints Health Education* has consciously sought to enable the teacher to address the Programmes of Study and Attainment Targets in core and foundation subjects of the National Curriculum while delivering a precise programme of health education in which the child is considered a valued contributor and benefactor.

Ultimately, *Blueprints Health Education Key Stage 1* seeks to facilitate the needs of the teacher in relation to planning, delivery, assessment and recording, and continuity and progression within a planned and coherent framework for health education. It is a cross curricular, thematic approach to the teaching of health education which, when used with *Blueprints Health Education Key Stage 2*, will have a spiral dimension enabling the extension and reinforcement of the learning process.

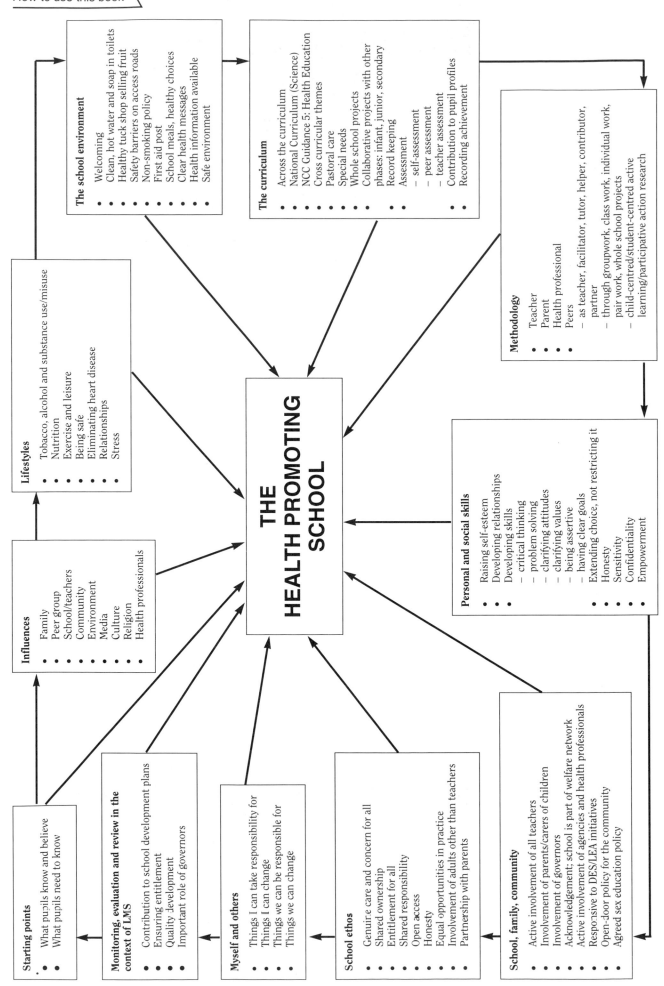

The school environment
- Welcoming
- Clean, hot water and soap in toilets
- Healthy tuck shop selling fruit
- Safety barriers on access roads
- Non-smoking policy
- First aid post
- School meals, healthy choices
- Clear health messages
- Health information available
- Safe environment

The curriculum
- Across the curriculum
- National Curriculum (Science)
- NCC Guidance 5: Health Education
- Cross curricular themes
- Pastoral care
- Special needs
- Whole school projects
- Collaborative projects with other phases: infant, junior, secondary
- Record keeping
- Assessment
  - self-assessment
  - peer assessment
  - teacher assessment
  - Contribution to pupil profiles
  - Recording achievement

Methodology
- Teacher
- Parent
- Health professional
- Peers
  - as teacher, facilitator, tutor, helper, contributor, partner
  - through groupwork, class work, individual work, pair work, whole school projects
  - child-centred/student-centred active learning/participative action research

Lifestyles
- Tobacco, alcohol and substance use/misuse
- Nutrition
- Exercise and leisure
- Being safe
- Eliminating heart disease
- Relationships
- Stress

Influences
- Family
- Peer group
- School/teachers
- Community
- Environment
- Media
- Culture
- Religion
- Health professionals

THE HEALTH PROMOTING SCHOOL

Personal and social skills
- Raising self-esteem
- Developing relationships
- Developing skills
  - critical thinking
  - problem solving
  - clarifying attitudes
  - clarifying values
  - being assertive
  - having clear goals
- Extending choice, not restricting it
- Honesty
- Sensitivity
- Confidentiality
- Empowerment

Starting points
- What pupils know and believe
- What pupils need to know

Monitoring, evaluation and review in the context of LMS
- Contribution to school development plans
- Ensuring entitlement
- Quality development
- Important role of governors

Myself and others
- Things I can take responsibility for
- Things I can change
- Things we can be responsible for
- Things we can change

School ethos
- Genuine care and concern for all
- Shared ownership
- Entitlement for all
- Shared responsibility
- Open access
- Honesty
- Equal opportunities in practice
- Involvement of adults other than teachers
- Partnership with parents

School, family, community
- Active involvement of all teachers
- Involvement of parents/carers of children
- Involvement of governors
- Acknowledgement; school is part of welfare network
- Active involvement of agencies and health professionals
- Responsive to DES/LEA initiatives
- Open-door policy for the community
- Agreed sex education policy

MEDICINES AND DRUGS

Building blocks of the curriculum

Citizenship

- Being responsible
- Saying 'no!'

History

- Medicines long ago

Mathematics

- Medicines in the house – survey
- Illnesses – survey
- Dosages
- Keeping medicines safe

Environment

- Keeping the environment safe

Geography

- Where do we get medicines from?
- Who keeps us well?
- Finding the clinic, doctor's surgery, hospital

English

- Making decisions
- Group drama
- Being assertive
- Peer group pressure
- Story sequencing

Economic and industrial awareness

- The chemist's shop

RE

- Healers and healing
- The story of people famous for their work as healers
- Stories from religious texts

Technology

- Keeping medicines safe

Science

- Smoking
- Lungs – exhaling and inhaling
- Making a smoking machine
- Substances around the home

Music

- Songs on the theme of medicines

PE

- Looking after our hearts and lungs

Art

- Staying healthy – collage work

INTRODUCTION

Research by the HEA Primary Schools Health Education project has shown that children between the ages of four and eleven have an ever increasing awareness of 'what makes and keeps them healthy' (Williams, Wetton and Moon, 1989). In this context it was found that children as young as four years of age had a drugs vocabulary which as they got older increasingly acknowledged the use of medicines, tobacco, alcohol and illegal substances. Similar research in Birmingham schools (Lloyd and Combes, 1988) also showed that children between the ages of five and eleven had knowledge and experience of tobacco and alcohol while some eleven-year-olds were able to make explicit links between the use of illegal drugs and HIV/AIDS. Clearly, neither schools nor parents can afford to dismiss this evidence if children are to be dissuaded from experimentation. **Medicines and drugs** is about enabling children to recognise the risks associated with substance use and to develop the skills necessary to lead healthy and safe lives.

Curriculum Guidance 5 learning objectives

Pupils should:

- know that all medicines are drugs but not all drugs are medicines.
- know that all substances can be harmful if not used properly.
- know about the different types of medicines and that some people need them to live a normal life.
- know and understand simple safety rules about medicines, tablets, solvents, household substances.

STARTING POINTS

C1

- Tell the children the following story: 'On the way to school this morning I found a small tin. I carefully opened the lid and saw some drugs inside'.

- Use **copymaster 1 (Who lost the tin?)** and ask the children to draw what they think is in the tin and the person they think has lost the tin. (Older pupils could be asked to write a description of the person they think has lost the tin.)

- Display the pictures/writing and ask them what they think is in the tin. Write their ideas on the board/large sheet of paper.

- Similarly, ask them who they think lost the tin and write down their suggestions. (In both cases add suggestions of your own.)

- Ask the children what things on their list of 'what is in the tin?' are harmful to people and which are not. Ask them if they think that medicines are harmful. Tell them that any substance is harmful if not used properly, and that they are going to find out all about medicines and drugs.

What is in the tin?

Heroin medicine throat sweets aspirins cigarettes

Who lost the tin?

a man a doctor a junkie a lady hippy sick person teacher

Science building block

AT1 L1, 2
AT2 L1, 2, 3

Science has an important contribution to make to the study of medicines and drugs. However, it is important to realise that children need more than information alone to be able to respond appropriately to situations.

SCIENCE ACTIVITIES

Air

1 Ask the children what they think air is:

- can they see it?
- can they feel it?
- can they smell it?
- does it have any colour?
- can they hear it?

2 Give each child a balloon and tell them to blow it up, then release the air gradually. Can they feel the air coming out? Can they hear the air coming out?

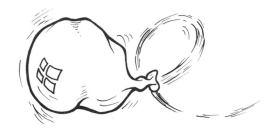

3 Give each child a straw and a piece of tissue paper. The paper can be cut into the shape of a fish. Tell the children to blow through the straw and make the shape move across the table top (or make a small aquarium using a shoebox lid or something similar).

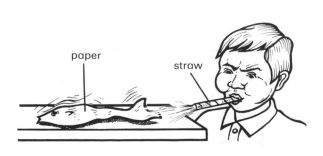

4 Make some 'matchbox' boats or simply place corks in water and allow the children to propel them across the water by blowing.

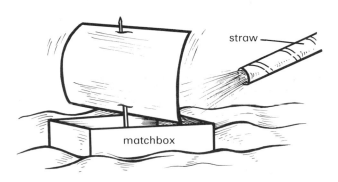

5 Group or individual pictures can be created by giving the children a mixture of paints and a straw. Ask them to blow the paint across the paper. Interesting and sometimes spectacular creations can be formed when colours collide and mix.

Always point out to children that they are continually inhaling air and exhaling using the air around them and passing it through their lungs.

6 Although a good mathematics activity, this is probably the appropriate place to introduce taking and observing differences in chest and tummy measurements in relation to breathing air in and out. It is an important awareness raising exercise in understanding what happens when we breathe. Children can do this in pairs and the before/after results can be recorded on a chart.

7 Ask the children what they saw for each activity:

- what did they do? (this should include preparing the activity)
- what did they see?
- what can they now say about air?

Lungs

1 Ask the children what is in the air that we need to stay alive. What would happen if we were deprived of air? Discuss the need for divers to have air supplies under water and for astronauts similarly to have an air supply. (Important: stress to children that they should never play with plastic bags and that they should always dispose of them safely.)

To demonstrate that air has oxygen place a candle on a saucer of water and place a jam jar over the top having lit the candle previously. As the candle uses up the oxygen, water will move up into the jar to replace it and the candle will go out.

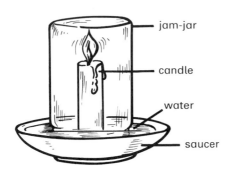

jam-jar

candle

water

saucer

2 With the help of **copymaster 2 (Experiment with air)** ask the children to observe what happens and to describe what they see. Ask them what happens to air when we breathe. Help them with words like windpipe, lungs, oxygen, carbon dioxide.

3 Using **copymaster 3 (Beetle drive)**, divide the class into groups of four and cut out enough shapes for the four players. Each player takes a turn to roll a die and pick up the corresponding piece. If they roll the same number, having already rolled it once, they miss a turn. The first player to complete a set is the winner.

4 Make a collection of substances found in the home that children should not smell because to do so would damage their ability to breathe.

Things we should not smell or play with

Smoking

1 Ask the children how we might damage our lungs. Write down their ideas.

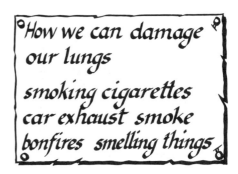

How we can damage our lungs
smoking cigarettes
car exhaust smoke
bonfires smelling things

2 Ask them what effects smoke has on them – coughing, running eyes, blocked up nose, etc.

3 Create a simple smoking machine by placing a cigarette into a tube, making it airtight by placing plasticine round the joins and placing the tubes into a transparent plastic/polythene bottle, partially filled with cotton wool. (For closer observation it is recommended that several machines are made.)

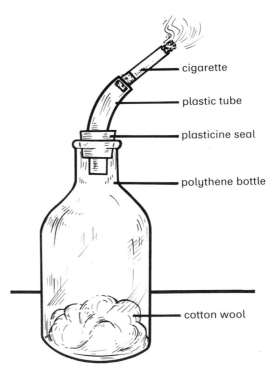

cigarette

plastic tube

plasticine seal

polythene bottle

cotton wool

Take the smoking machine outside or into an open space and light the cigarette. By squeezing the bottle gently the cigarette will 'smoke'.

Tell the children to look carefully at what happens in the bottle; suggest that the bottle is someone's lungs.

In the classroom, take the bottle apart and have the children look closely at the contents. (The inside of the machine will smell and be very unpleasant. The cotton wool in the bottle itself will be discoloured.)

4

4 Ask the children to describe what they see.

smelly slimey sticky yellow brown dirty horrible

5 The following questions could form the basis of a questionnaire or worksheet:

- what does the machine look like?
- why are seals placed around the plastic straw and the cork stopper and where the cigarette is fixed to the straw?
- what happens when the side of the bottle is squeezed?
- what happens to the cotton wool in the bottle?
- what colour is the cigarette smoke?
- what colour is the cotton wool after the smoke has been in the bottle for a while?
- what is the name of the brown substance given off from the cigarette?
- what might happen to a person's lungs if they smoke for a long time?

6 Ask the children if they think that smoking cigarettes is a good idea; what might happen to people who smoke? Point out the Government health warning on the side of a packet of cigarettes. Do not overstress people dying as some children will have parents or relatives at home who smoke. It is better to emphasise coughs, ill-health and the positive benefits of not smoking.

Mathematics building block

AT1 L1, 2, 3
AT2 L1, 2
AT4 L1, 2, 3
AT5 L2

Medicines come in measured amounts. To take more than is needed can be dangerous. Never take medicines unless given to us by those who care for us.

MATHEMATICS ACTIVITIES

C4

1 Ask the children to tell you of the medicines that they may have had and what they took them for. Write down their ideas.

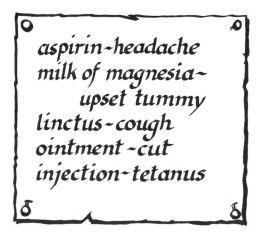

aspirin-headache
milk of magnesia-
  upset tummy
linctus-cough
ointment -cut
injection-tetanus

Ask them who gives them these medicines; where did the medicine come from?

mummy and daddy
doctor nurse
hospital chemist
supermarket clinic
health centre

2 Using the list of medicines that the children generated ask the class who used each on the list. Record the numbers on a chart. Ask the children to state which is the most common medicine, the most common form of medicine (ointment, tablet, syrup, powder, etc.), the least common medicine.

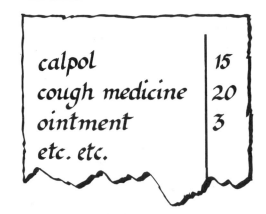

calpol	15
cough medicine	20
ointment	3
etc. etc.	

drums, big bottles, small bottles, etc. Label each clearly according to size and shape. Add the caption 'We should never take medicines unless given to us by someone who cares for us' to the display.

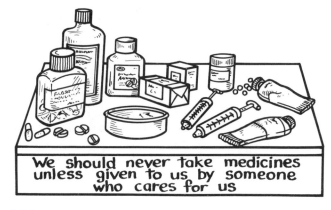

We should never take medicines unless given to us by someone who cares for us

3 Use this information to draw simple histograms or pictograms to show medicines we take in our class.

4 Similarly, record illnesses the children have had by listing the information in chart form.

5 Bring in different examples of medicines and their containers. Discuss with the children that medicines come in different forms and shapes – capsules, pills, powders, liquids, creams, ointments, drops – and that they are usually swallowed, rubbed or injected. Use **copymaster 4 (Containers and shapes)** and when the children have matched the containers to the corresponding shapes, introduce them to the name for each shape (box, cylinder, tube, etc.).

6 Read the instructions from some of the packages/containers to the children. Ask them why they should never take more than the recommended dosage.

7 Consider why medicines should always be stored in a lockable cupboard/container well out of reach of small children.

8 Ask the children to obtain their parents' permission and bring in as many different types of empty medicine containers as they can. Then place them on a table to make sets. Sets of: packages, tubes,

9 Discuss with the children where things like cleaners, polish, petrol, glue and weedkillers should be stored.

10 Together as a class, make up some simple rules for being safe with medicines, household, garage and garden substances. Write down their ideas and then use them to make posters to emphasise the rules.

RULES
- never take pills or medicine without mummy or daddy knowing
- don't smell things in bottles or containers
- don't leave medicines lying about the house
- don't touch bottles in the garage or garden shed

English building block

AT1 L1, 2, 3
AT2 L1, 2, 3
AT4 L1, 2, 3
AT5 L1, 2

Making decisions about what action to take means knowing what is right and what is wrong. Sometimes there are options available; often there is confusion between medicines being good and being harmful, the role model given by adults in relation to smoking, alcohol and drug-taking and the clueless terminology of medicines, substances and drugs. These can begin to be addressed through the teaching of language skills.

ENGLISH ACTIVITIES

C5–7

1 Remind the children of the story you told them about the lost tin and the drugs that were in it and what they thought was in the tin (see **Starting points**). Ask them what they would have done if they had found the tin. What would they have done with it; who would they have told?

2 Tell the children the story of Goldilocks and the Three Bears (this is a good story to consider from many aspects of personal safety). Particularly draw attention to Goldilocks trying what she thought was porridge, and despite the awful taste of the first dish, she still persists in trying the others.

3 Now ask the children what they would have done if they found something in a bowl on the table. What should Goldilocks have done? Using **copymaster 5 (What's on the shelf?)**, ask the children to indicate which container they think is 'safe'. Emphasise that old containers are often used for dangerous substances and that labels can be misleading.

4 In small groups ask the children to rehearse their ideas in role-play and then each group in turn presents their play to the rest of the class.

5 Ask them what they would do if someone 'dared' them to smell or taste something which they didn't recognise or to have a 'puff' on a cigarette.

6 Discuss with them how they might say 'No' and mean it (see **Being safe**, p. 41) or what they might do. Write down their ideas.

7 Using **copymaster 6 (Katie's medicine)**, ask the children to cut up the sheet and place the pictures and the story in the correct order. They may wish to colour the pictures and stick them on to a strip of card or paper and then write their own story to go with the pictures.

8 Finally, suggest that the children complete **copymaster 7 (Words)** and then write a sentence using the words from the copymaster in the appropriate context.

Geography building block

AT1 L1, 2, 3
AT2 L1, 2, 3
AT4 L1, 2
AT5 L1, 2, 3

Teaching children to be cautious of medicines is, of course, important but equally important is the need to impress upon them that medicines are beneficial to their good health. Medicines are given by those who care for us and can be obtained from places in the locality. Identifying those places can be a task achieved through an exercise in local geography.

GEOGRAPHY ACTIVITIES

C8

1 Remind the children of where they usually got their medicines from: doctor's surgery, chemist, clinic, hospital, supermarket, etc. (see p. 5).

2 Using a large-scale map of the school's locality or redrawn from an A–Z, ask the children their address and help them to find it on the map. For each child mark it with a coloured flag (or a pin).

3 Ask the children similarly to find their doctor's surgery, the clinic, chemist shops and supermarkets selling medicines, etc. on the map.

4 Discuss who else helps us in the community. Write down their suggestions.

police officer
crossing warden
fireman
ambulance driver

5 Ask the children to draw these people using **copymaster 8 (People who help us)** as a framework.

6 See if any of the people/places mentioned can be marked on the map.

7 Now draw lines or place strings/rubber bands on the map to make squares. Give each square across the top of the map a letter and each square down the edge of the map a number.

8 Ask the children to say in which square they live. Give the co-ordinates A1, B1, C4, etc. Which square is the doctor in, the chemist, etc.? (This can be linked with similar work on **Being safe** (see p. 44).)

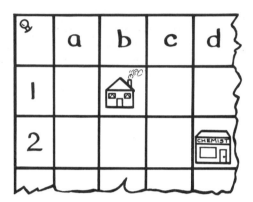

History building block

AT1 L2, 3
AT2 L1, 3
AT3 L1, 2, 3

The prescribing and taking of medicines goes back to at least 5,000 years ago when the Ancient Sumerians, who were based around the Tigris and Euphrates rivers which flow through modern Iraq, left clay tablets on which Sumerian doctors prescribed medicines prepared from seeds, resin and herbs. History can introduce to young children the notion of the development of medicines over a period of time.

HISTORY ACTIVITIES ▶

1 Together, say the poem 'Ring a Ring of Roses'. Ask the class what they think a posy is. Tell them how, a long time ago, an illness caused by germs caught from the bite of a rat flea, killed a lot of people in England. People then thought that by having a posy of sweet-smelling flowers to smell and hold close to their nose and mouth they wouldn't get ill. (It would be useful to show pictures of clothes worn during the middle ages, houses and information on the general way of life at the time of the Plague.) Differences between then and now,

particularly health related (i.e. drinking water, personal hygiene, sanitation, preservation and preparation of food, etc.) could be discussed. Ask the children if they think smelling a posy could work. If not, why?

2 Make posies by using circular tissue paper for flowers and straws for stems. The posy can be wrapped in a doily.

Technology building block

AT1 L1, 2, 3
AT2 L1, 2, 3
AT3 L1, 2, 3
AT4 L1, 2, 3

Satisfying needs and addressing opportunities is an important element in the process of technology. Key Stage 1 of the National Curriculum states this quite specifically. **Medicines and drugs** considers this in the context of safe and usable tops for medicine containers.

TECHNOLOGY ACTIVITIES

1 Provide the class with an assortment of plastic bottles and tablet containers with an array of tops, especially those designed to be 'child proof' and easy for arthritic fingers to open.

2 In groups, ask the children to see how easily they can open the bottles and containers; placing them in sets according to how easy or difficult they are. (They should record their results on paper.)

3 Discuss with the children why making a medicine container safe for children can sometimes mean making it difficult for people who cannot hold the bottle/container or who, through illness, have not got the strength needed to open the top.

4 Place on a table some tools commonly found in a toolbox at home. Label the tools and then ask the

children which of the tools seen on the table might help a person to unscrew a top (i.e. adjustable spanner, pliers, mole-wrench, measuring calipers, etc.).

5 Ask the children to observe some of these tools and to draw carefully a tool from their close observation, paying strict attention to detail.

6 Using **copymaster 9 (Opening bottles)**, ask them to draw an idea they might have for helping elderly or infirm people to open bottles easily.

7 Suggest that using junk materials, children could make a tool that could help elderly or infirm people to open bottles. (This may not be a very practical task for young children but will enable them to focus on the difficulties elderly and infirm people face.)

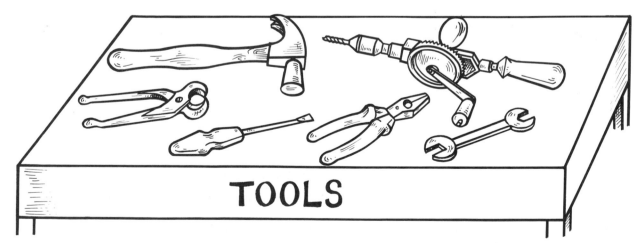

TOOLS

PE building block

Tell children that if people do no look after their heart and lungs by exercising, by not smoking and by eating the right food, they could become very ill and have to take medicines in order to save their life.

9

PE ACTIVITIES

1 Remind children that when we exercise our hearts have to work faster to pump our blood around our bodies to transport the oxygen from our lungs to where it is needed.

2 While standing still and quiet tell the children to place one hand on their chest and to feel the way their heart beats. Is their heart beating quickly or slowly? Are they breathing quickly or slowly?

3 Have the children step up on to benches and to step down ten times, with the left foot leading and ten times with the right foot leading.

4 Now tell the children to repeat the hand on the chest activity. What differences are there?

5 Repeat this two or three times and then tell the them to lie on the floor letting their bodies relax and go all floppy. After a few minutes repeat the hand on chest activity. What do they notice? Why has their heart beat slowed down?

6 Ask the children how they might stop their lungs working properly. Reinforce the 'smoking messages' and, having done the smoking machine activity (see p. 4), remind the class of what they saw, or get them to tell you what they saw.

Art building block

Visual images are very strong, universal ways of sending messages and making statements.

ART ACTIVITIES

There are a number of art-specific activities already suggested in this section. Here are three additional ones.

1 Using advertisements from magazines for cigarettes and alcohol, create collages with a 'Don't smoke' or 'Be safe with medicines' theme. Display the collages in the classroom.

2 Use **copymaster 10 (Danger – poison!)** and ask the children to design a label that would warn people that the content of the bottle is poisonous.

3 Make a collage of shelves in a chemist shop. Label some of the medicines.

RE building block

The theme of healers and healing is strongly defined and represented throughout most religious faiths. Children particularly enjoy stories of real people whose faith and love of mankind lead them to making great unselfish acts and personal sacrifices.

RE ACTIVITIES ▶

1 Tell the story of one or more of the following:

- Florence Nightingale, who organised the nursing of sick and wounded soldiers during the Crimean war.
- Mother Teresa, who cares for sick and orphaned children abandoned on the streets of Calcutta.
- Elizabeth Garrett, the first English woman doctor.
- Edith Cavell, a nurse who helped wounded soldiers in enemy territory.
- Mary Secole, a black nurse.

(Make a special reference to the fact that all are women.)

2 Ask the children about people they know who are kind to them and help them when they are sick. Suggest that they write about those people.

Other stories of a similar theme can be told: 'Guru Nanak and the Leper' (Assembly Stories from Around the World, W. Dargue, OUP 1983). Jesus healing the sick (Luke 17:11–19; Mark 7:31–5).

3 Suggest the children write their own prayer on the theme of healing.

Mary Secole, a black nurse at Crimea, was born in Jamaica in 1805. Mary learned traditional medicine and natural cures from her mother.
In 1854 she set up a 'hospital' to feed hundreds of wounded and dying soldiers.
She died in 1881 and was buried in London.

Music building block

There are a number of songs on the theme of medicine that can be sung with piano, guitar and simple percussion accompaniment.

- Ten green bottles (from *Count Me In*)
- I think I've caught a cold (from *Harlequin*)
- Miss Polly (from *Okki Tokk* – Unga)
- John Brown's baby (from *Okki Tokk* – Unga)
- Lilly the Pink (from *Appuskido*)

ASSESSMENT ▶

Where appropriate, match activities to the Programmes of Study for 'core and foundation' subjects.

At an individual level

1 For Mathematics: handling data (i.e. choose criteria to sort and classify objects; record results of observations, procedure and outcomes) – for the activity relating to Technology and the sorting of bottle caps/tops into how easily they open, assess the child's ability to record according to the criteria and the ability to undertake the task correctly.

2 For Science: life and living processes (i.e. know that personal hygiene, food, exercise, rest and safety and the safe use of medicines are important) – for the smoking machine activity ask the children to write in their own words what they did and what they saw. They could draw pictures to illustrate. Were they knowledgeable of the health message about smoking?

3 For English: speaking and listening (i.e. listen attentively to stories and poems, and talk about them) – there are plenty of opportunities to assess children's capacity to express themselves effectively in a variety of speaking and listening activities, matching style and response to audience and purpose throughout the topic of medicines and drugs.

At a group level

1 Have all the children sit in a circle and tell them that in turn they have to complete a sentence. Remind them that when someone is talking they should listen carefully and not interrupt.

2 Ask them to sit very quietly and to think of all the things they have learned about medicines and drugs.

3 Now in the circle ask each child in turn to complete the sentence

'Something that I learned about medicines and drugs was …'

If a child cannot think of something immediately, pass on and continue round the circle, coming back to those children at the end. (It doesn't matter if children complete the sentence with the same information.)

4 Sum up the things that the children have said they have learned.

GROWING UP

Building blocks of the curriculum

Citizenship

- Being responsible to, and for, others; helping children to grow into adults

History

- The family tree
- Understanding the concept of time in relation to growing up
- Memories

English

- Feeling good – writing and role-play about feeling good and making others happy

Environment

- Being responsible to the environment

RE

- The lives of the great spiritual leaders; Jesus as a child, etc.

Technology

- Knowing that a system is made up of related parts which are combined for a purpose
- Making Jumping Jack

Economic and industrial awareness

- Jobs – who does what?
- Which jobs are important?

Science

- Understanding similarities and differences between male and female; parts of the body; the skeleton

Art

- Expressions of feelings through drawing, painting and making activities

PE

- Exercise for building bones and muscles

Mathematics

- Changing and growing
- Measuring and observing

INTRODUCTION

From a very early age children are subject to endless images of sex, sexuality, gender, roles and stereotypes of particular forms of behaviour. Most of these images are presented by television, films, magazines and newspapers and are often, for good or ill, reinforced in the home. Parental attitudes to sexual situations whether in the home or as seen on television, will certainly influence children's own attitudes. It is important, therefore, to be sensitive to 'the views of those parents whose ethnic background and religious or other beliefs may cause them to hold reservations about such work' in school (HMI, 1986).

Young children are generally very interested in their own bodies and an understanding of how their bodies work is not only relevant but also important for the development of a positive self-concept. Simply responding to 'children's questions' is not sufficient because unless situations are created whereby children can ask questions openly and receive appropriate answers, questions will seldom be asked. What is required is a structured and systematic approach relating to the children's stage of development and in which such work is presented 'in the context of family life, loving relationships and respect for others: in short, within a moral framework' (HMI, 1986).

Schools are reminded that the Education Act (No. 2) 1986 previously made the decision as to whether sex education should form part of the curriculum or not the responsibility of the governors. This has been superseded by the Education Reform Act (ERA) 1988, which places elements of sex education in the statutory National Curriculum for Science through Attainment Target 2: Life and Living Processes. Schools, therefore, have a legal obligation to ensure that sex education is taught in the curriculum. However, schools should continue to keep up to date a separate written statement of the school's policy in relation to sex education as required by the 1986 Act.

Curriculum Guidance 5 learning objectives

Pupils should:

- know that humans develop at different rates and that human babies have special needs.
- be able to name parts of the body including the reproductive system (external) and understand the concept of male and female.
- know about personal safety, e.g. know that individuals have rights over their own bodies and that there are differences between good and bad touches; begin to develop skills and practices which will help maintain personal safety.
- appreciate ways in which people learn to live and work together; listening, discussing, sharing.

STARTING POINTS

- Ask each child to bring in photographs of themselves as babies and, if possible, a recent photograph.

- Request that the children find out from their parents or the people at home who look after them, where they were born, how much they weighed,

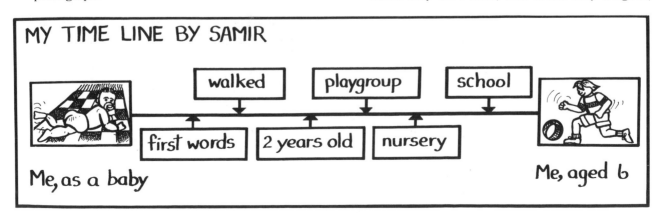

MY TIME LINE BY SAMIR

walked   playgroup   school

first words   2 years old   nursery

Me, as a baby   Me, aged 6

who they are supposed to look like, why they have the names they do, when they said their first words, walked, went to playgroup and so on. (Be sensitive to those children for whom this might be difficult.)

- Mount the photographs at either end of large strips of paper and draw a line between them.

- Discuss the things they have found out as a class and, using **copymaster 11 (My time line)**, help the children to record key events in their lives on the 'time line'.

- Consider with the children what things they can do for themselves now which they couldn't when they were babies. Write down their suggestions and observations.

> feed themselves
> go to the toilet
> get dressed
> go to the shops
> look after self
> go swimming
> go to school
> wash self

- Ask who did those things for them when they were babies.

- Referring to the 'time lines' which should be displayed around the classroom, ask them if they are all the same. (The important thing to note is that people grow at different rates and that we are all special and unique.)

- Ask the class what they think all babies need.

> love, warmth,
> sleep, care,
> a mummy,
> cleaning,
> a daddy,
> milk, nappies

- Invite a mum with a new baby to come to school to talk to the children. Tell the children that they are going to find out about themselves and where they came from and how they have grown from being helpless babies into the big, energetic children they are today.

- You may wish at this stage to ask the class in a general way where they think they came from. Do not 'tell the children off' for what may appear to an adult to be a silly answer. Many children believe, through misinformation gathered from family and peers, some very strange stories indeed!

Science building block

| AT2 L1, 2, 3 | Understanding similarities and differences between the concept of male and female is vital to a positive self-concept. |

SCIENCE ACTIVITIES

C12 –14

The body

1. Divide the class into groups. Each group should be mixed. Give each group a very large sheet of white paper (this can be made up of several sheets previously stuck together).

2. Tell the children that one of them in the group should lie on the paper and that using pencils the others should carefully draw around them.

3. Ask the children to name as many parts of the body as they can. Write the names up on the chalkboard or a large sheet of paper for all to see.

4. Tell the children to mark on their 'person' outlines the parts of their bodies in the appropriate space.

5. Visit each group in turn and ask them to draw on the body the parts that make boys and girls different. (They may already have done this.)

6. Ask each group in turn to display their person drawing and to tell the class the details of their labelling. (Pin each up around the classroom.)

7. Discuss with the class the physical difference between boys and girls (and all males and females). Tell

them that we may have 'personal' names for some parts of the body, e.g. Willy, which is perfectly acceptable. However, do tell them that the correct words are penis for boys and vagina for girls. Keep explanations very simple and be ready to explain why males have a penis and females have a vagina.

8 Use **copymaster 12 (Making pairs)** and ask the children to match pairs by drawing connecting lines to the correct pictures.

The skeleton

1 Ask the children what keeps them standing up straight. Why don't they collapse in a heap? If you can get hold of a skeleton from your science or health education adviser, show how some bones protect vital parts of our body like the skull and the ribs while other bones move to help us walk or lift things.

2 Have the children look carefully at the skeleton and on black paper, using white paint, draw the skeleton.

3 If you are unable to get a skeleton, discuss the purpose of bones and then have the children cut out **Jumping Jack** from **copymaster 13**. Paper fasteners can be used to articulate the limbs. Hang these up as mobiles.

4 Tell the class it doesn't matter if they are male or female – everybody has a skeleton to support their bodies.

Mathematics building block

AT1 L1, 2, 3
AT2 L1, 2, 3
AT4 L1, 2, 3
AT5 L1, 2, 3

It is important to recognise that we are growing and changing all of the time and that we are all different.

MATHEMATICS ACTIVITIES

C14
–16

1 Discuss with the children the things they have grown out of. Record their ideas and ask them to bring in examples for display in the classroom. Using **copymaster 14 (I'm too big for these!)**, remind them of the things that they said they could do for themselves now, but couldn't do as babies, and ask them to draw pictures of things they have grown out of or no longer use.

> baby clothes,
> car seat, cot,
> pram, push-chair,
> shoes, high-chair

2 With the children in groups have them measure and record their heights and weights, and then using **copymaster 15 (Measuring)**, encourage them to make comparisons taking up appropriate vocabulary – bigger than, smaller than, shorter than, heavier than, and so on. When weighing and measuring, different units of weight and length could be used: i.e. bean bags, building blocks of the same size, hand spans, shoe lengths, etc.

3 Suggest that each group compares the tallest and shortest, the heaviest and lightest measurements to make comparisons for the whole class.

4 Each child could record their details on **copymaster 16 (My name is ...)**, writing in their name, height and weight. The figure could be cut out, mounted and displayed around the classroom.

5 Pin some very large sheets of paper to the wall and in groups have the children record how high they can reach. (Use a different colour for each child in the group.)

6 Do this standing still and then record how high they can reach by jumping.

7 The children should record the heights reached from the floor in each case and work out the difference between the two.

8 As for the height and weight, have the children note who in their group and who in the class can reach the highest and so on. Then compare the names recorded with the names for tallest, shortest, heaviest, lightest.

The tallest person in our class is [_____]
who is _____ *units/metres tall*

[_____] *is the shortest person in our class*
and is _____ *units/metres tall*

RAZIA — 1 metre 10 — 30 kilos

KATIE — 1 metre 5 — 25 kilos

9 Ask the class if the names are the same. If they are, what can they say about the relationship between the two sets of numbers? Can they make up a rule? e.g. the tallest person can jump reach the highest, therefore tall people can reach further than short people (or there is no relationship between height and reach if those names are not the same).

10 Other comparisons could be completed using such variables as shoe size, hand span and arm sizes.

11 Ask the class if there is any difference between the boys in the class and the girls. Reinforce the idea that both girls and boys may be the tallest, lightest, reach the furthest, etc.

- **Note** These exercises can be repeated later in the year and the differences compared.

PE building block

Exercise in an important factor in children's development, not least for building strong bones and developing muscles.

PE ACTIVITIES ▶

1 Remind the children of the things they could not do as babies. Ask the class what things they can do now: run, jump, hop, run backwards, gambols, somersaults, etc.

2 Have the children running into space in the hall or playground. On command:

- run backwards
- hop on left, then right foot
- somersault forwards/backwards (on mats)
- throw a ball
- jump with both feet together
- run slowly, run fast
- catch a ball
- kick a ball

3 Divide the class into teams and have relay races for each of the above activities.

4 Following the exercise, ask the children if their body feels different, and to say where and what the difference is, i.e. legs ache, breathing is quicker.

5 Ask the children what things they think they are good at and which ones they think they need to practise. Ask each child to tell the class in turn (see Things I Can Do, *Blueprints Topics*, p. 15, Myself 6).

6 Tell the children that they need exercise to help them grow and develop and that the more they practise running, jumping, etc. the better they will become.

> I am good at _____ but
> I need to practise _____

Art building block

Recognising feelings and emotions in ourselves and others is an important part of growing up. The expression of feelings through drawing, painting and making activities enable art to facilitate this part of a person's development if approached with sensitivity.

ART ACTIVITIES

1 Prepare a large sheet of paper, on which children will be able to paint, by drawing three face shapes.

SAD   ANGRY   HAPPY

2 With the children working in pairs and facing each other, tell them to make sad, angry and happy faces. Ask them how they know which is which. This activity can be linked to the children's discussions about feelings (see pp. 19–20).

3 Tell the children to paint sad, angry and happy portraits of the person facing them. This is an opportunity to discuss and illustrate the need for careful observation of the subject and particularly to refer to proportion in relation to a person's face.

4 Ask the class how they think they could change their partner's sad face into a happy face. What could they do for them that would make them happy?

5 Display the portraits with a statement made by each partner.

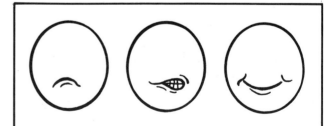

I can make Luanne happy by playing with her.

18

English building block

> AT1 L1, 2, 3
> AT2 L1, 2
> AT3 L1, 2

Growing up is not only a physical development, it is also a development of personal independence based on an understanding of ourselves and others.

The Programme of Study in English Key Stage 1 of the National Curriculum emphasises the need for children to respond to, work with and be involved in collaborative and exploratory learning, adjust to, listen and give weight to, the opinions of others, etc. All such direction is very supportive of the children's search for knowing how they feel about themselves and others.

ENGLISH ACTIVITIES

Feeling happy

1 Explain to the children that the class is going to think about all the things that make each one of them feel good. The discussion might focus on the idea that feeling good means feeling happy.

2 First of all ask each child to tell the others what makes them feel happy. Using the board or a large sheet of paper the teacher can record all/some of the replies or select key words. (This can be linked with **Being safe**, English building block activity 11, p. 41.)

3 Suggest to the children that as these seem such good ideas the class will share them with visitors to the classroom. Using **copymaster 17 (Happy balloons)**, arrange for the children to cut the balloon shapes out and paint them in different colours. On each balloon will be a sentence or words saying what makes each child happy. The balloons can be mounted and attractively displayed.

4 Discuss with the children that feeling happy can come about through doing something or owning something; sometimes it can happen when we see something or are with someone; sometimes it is through giving and receiving, sharing and helping. Seek examples of all these from the class.

5 Divide the class into groups of four five or six. Give each group a picture taken from **copymaster 18 (Happy endings)** and ask them to make up a play or story which has something to do with the picture they have been

given and must result in someone being made very happy.

6 Tell the children what makes you, as a teacher, happy. List all the things that the children do, and that you hope they will do, that results in making you happy. Make the point that as they grow up they will be expected to do more and more, both in school and at home – especially for themselves, and in doing so, should always try to consider other people.

7 Following the work the children have undertaken, brainstorm the class and list on a large sheet of paper/board things children can do to make others happy. Write these down on the petals of a large paper flower and display.

8 Round off with **copymaster 19 (Finding happiness)**. The children might like to attempt the maze and then state or draw a picture representing what they think happiness is once they reach it.

History building block

| AT1 L1, 2, 3 |
| AT2 L1, 2, 3 |
| AT3 L1, 2, 3 |

History at Key Stage 1 adopts a straightforward approach intended to introduce pupils to the idea of time and to people viewed in a historical dimension, particularly in relation to the questions 'Who am I?' and 'Where am I?' **Growing up** addresses both of these concepts.

HISTORY ACTIVITIES

1 Set the children the task of discovering the dates of birth of those in their family. It need not include every member, but as many as possible. The information can be recorded on **copymaster 20 (My family tree)**. (Please note that this is not a family tree in the truest sense, but is a pictorial means of gathering and viewing information.)

2 Taking all the details gained from the 'family tree' exercise, ask the children to write out the names of

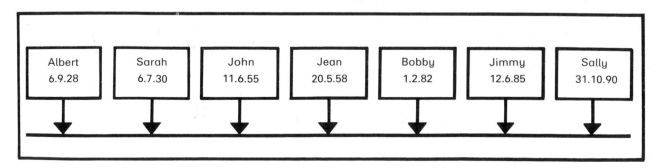

members of the family and relatives with each one's date of birth. Ask them to arrange their information starting with the very youngest member on the right and working towards the left where the last person placed will be the oldest member of the family they know.

3 Invite the children to ask their parents or someone who cares for them, to tell them about an early memory they have of them when they were very little. Encourage them to report back and share the story with the others in the class. Suggest that they find out about a memory that an older person they know has of themselves when they were young.

Technology building block

AT1 L1
AT3 L1, 2
AT4 L1, 2

In technology, the National Curriculum suggests that Key Stage 1 pupils should be taught to:

- 'know that a system is made of related parts which are combined for a purpose'
- 'explore and use a variety of materials to design and make things'
- 'recognise that materials can be linked in various ways to make or allow movements'.

TECHNOLOGY ACTIVITIES

 C13

1 Re-use **copymaster 13 (Jumping Jack)** and glue the parts on to a sheet of card in order to stiffen the body. Each part is named. Consider the parts with the name showing to be the back of the model. The front can therefore be dressed or coloured according to personal choice. When winged pins have been placed in the appropriate holes connecting the joints, cotton or string can be drawn through the pins to a central piece, enabling the arms and legs to move up and down.

2 Have a simple quiz:

1) How many pin joints has Jumping Jack got?
2) Where else could joints be added?

3) What is the upper part of the leg called?
4) What part of the body does the head rest on?
5) What joint connects the lower and upper part of the arm?
6) What is the lower part of the body, which is joined to the top part of the legs, called?
7) Which joint connects our feet to our legs?
8) Which joint connects our hands to our arms?

3 String makes Jumping Jack move. Ask the children to form pairs and discuss together (a) how the model moves; (b) how the model was made.

RE building block

Young children's concepts of the great spiritual leaders are sometimes based on almost supernatural and mystical beings far removed from the actual origins which early scriptures described and emphasise. Here is an opportunity to inform or remind children that the leaders of the great religions were once children like themselves and learned a great deal from their parents and those around them before going forth into the wider world and preaching their beliefs.

RE ACTIVITIES

1 Tell the class that all the great prophets, teachers and gurus of the great religions had parents. Some children or their parents might come into school and tell you about the early life of a prophet or religious leader.

2 Focus on the childhood of one of the spiritual leaders. If there is little known about the childhood experiences of a guru or prophet then consider the place and time of the person's birth and imagine what it might have been like.

3 The early life of Jesus is fairly well chronicled from the momentous time of his birth, the story of which is familiar to most children, to his early adolescence.

- Make a comparison between the birth of Jesus and that of each child's; where did it take place? Who was there? Who attended to the birth and what happened afterwards?
- Who brought Jesus up? (What does the term 'brought up' mean?) What do we learn before we go to school? Who teaches us? Who is responsible for us? (What does responsible mean?)

4 Make whatever comparisons are possible between the child's own experiences and those of Jesus, pointing out both differences and similarities.

ASSESSMENT

1 Ask the children to complete the following prompts.

Three things I could not do as a baby were:

1) ....

2) ....

3) ....

Three things I can do for myself at home are:

1) ....

2) ....

3) ....

Three things I can do in my classroom/at school:

1) ....

2) ....

3) ....

Something I would like to be able to do when I am grown up is ....

....

Something I can help someone else to do is ....

....

Boys and girls can ....

....

It is important for children to have self-awareness and to recognise what they are able to do and would like to do, but it is equally important for children not to be constrained by their gender.

2 Using **copymaster 21 (As I grow up)**, ask the children to write about, or draw a picture to show, what they can do for themselves now that they are growing up.

FAMILIES

Building blocks of the curriculum

Citizenship

- Who cares for the family needs
- Responsibilities
- Civic services
- Public health, fire
- Police, doctor, teacher

PE

- Family exercises – exercises for in the home, with the family

Art

- Designing a family badge

Economic and industrial awareness

- Buying for the family needs – shopping lists, budgets
- Who does the shopping? (gender issues)
- Where does the family shop?
- Who pays?
- Cost

Science

- Studying other life forms, rearing a pet

Mathematics

- Tallest/shortest, heaviest/lightest, young/old

RE

- Major religious festivals as family celebrations
- Weddings

Geography

- Families and leisure: where do they go and what do they do?

Music

- Songs that promote positive images of the family

History

- Family stories: investigating changes in their own lives and those of their family or adults around them

English

- Our family stories

Technology

- Making family badges

INTRODUCTION

There is no such thing as a 'normal family' so the question 'what is a family?' is a particularly important one. As Pugh and De'Ath (1984) point out, 'Britain is a multicultural society and cultural diversities which are expressed through different child-rearing patterns and attitudes to family life' need to be recognised and valued. There are single parent families (through remarriage and adoption) families who have handicapped children and for some children, 'family life' relates to those who supervise them in the homes or centres in which they have been placed by social services or the courts.

Kate Torkington (1985) maintains that 'To make valid choices and decisions in relation to family life, young people need to have access to information of a factual kind and a balanced presentation of differing views on marriage and family life'. Clearly, such work needs to be developed sensitively and carefully in the classroom and teachers need to be particularly mindful of the situations and needs of individual children. However, this should not become a hindrance to such work; work in which pupils increasingly 'understand and value the central role of the family as an institution and the important part it plays in the development of attachment, love and concern' (NCC, 1990).

Curriculum Guidance 5 learning objectives

Pupils should:

- know that there are different types of family and be able to describe the roles of individuals within the family.
- know about rituals associated with birth, marriage and death and be able to talk about the emotions involved.
- understand the idea of growing from young to old.
- acquire the skills of caring for young animals for a limited time, under supervision.

STARTING POINTS

C22

- Ask the children which groups, clubs or organisations they belong to. Write these down on a large sheet of paper or the board.

> church   brownies
> temple dancing
> woodcraft   folk
> school
> cubs class 2 family
> swimming club
> karate riding mosque

- Make sure that the word 'family' is on your list.

- Tell them that we belong to all sorts of groups but the family is the most important.

- Invite the children to explain why their families are so important. Write down their ideas as before.

> look after us   take us on
> give us food   holiday
> buy us nice tell us stories
> clothes   give us toys on
> love us   our birthdays
>   make us better
>   when we're
>   sick

- Give each child a large piece of paper and tell them to draw or paint a picture of their family and to include themselves in the picture. Tell them that the lessons are going to be all about families. The children could make finger puppets, using **copymaster 22 (Finger families)**. In each shape a member of the family can be drawn. Then they should cut along the dotted line and glue the sides together. Be ready to give the children more shapes for additional family members.

- **Note** Throughout this unit, be sensitive to those children for whom being a member of a family can be a very negative experience.

Art/Technology building block

AT2 L1, 2, 3

The importance of valuing the contribution of each member of the family.

ART/TECHNOLOGY ACTIVITIES

C23

Family badges

1 Invite the children to tell each other what members of their family are good at. (They should include themselves also.) Then invite the class to share what members of their family are good at.

2 Tell the children that important and famous families like the Royal Family have special badges called 'coats of arms'. Tell them that they are going to design their own badge to show important things that members of their family do and are good at.

3 Using **copymaster 23 (Family badge)**, the children can design, draw and colour the shield to represent their family (see also *Blueprints Topics*, Knights and Castles 2, Shields p. 123).

4 The children can cut their badges or shields out and mount them on card. Write their names underneath and display them in the classroom.

5 Bring in some books or pictures of coats of arms for the children to see.

Samir   Tarik   Winston   Bina

Kevin   Tarsem   Julie   Kuldip

Class 2 : Our Family Badges

History building block

AT1 L1, 2, 3
AT2 L1, 2, 3
AT3 L1, 2

Family stories can be an important source of historical evidence regarding events which took place in the past. The National Curriculum Council recommends that pupils at Key Stage 1 have opportunities to investigate 'changes in their own lives and those of their family or adults around them' (Programmes of Study, Key Stage 1 Levels 1–3, DES, History in the National Curriculum, March 1991, p. 13).

HISTORY ACTIVITIES

When I was young ...

1 Ask the children to find out from their parents or the person who looks after them stories of when they were babies or very small children. Tell them to listen carefully and to be able to re-tell their story in the classroom.

2 Invite the children to tell their story to the class. Was it a funny story, a happy story, or a sad story?

3 Tell the children to write down their story and to draw a picture to illustrate it. Some or all of the class could write their story on the computer or word processor.

4 Mount the stories and pictures on to large sheets of paper and make a book for display in the classroom.

Our family stories

5 Suggest to them that they ask their grandparents to tell them stories about when their mums and dads were babies/small children.

6 Invite them to bring in photographs and articles that represent particular events from their family's past. Display these in the classroom or create a time line round the classroom, placing the events in the appropriate place (see **Growing up**, p. 15).

Music building block

There are many songs which promote positive images of the 'family' in the broadest sense of the word.

MUSIC ACTIVITIES

The following suggestions for class songs are available from several sources.

Someone's Singing, Lord (A & C Black, 1984)
If I had a hammer
When I needed a neighbour
The ink is black, the page is white
At half past three we go home to tea

Apuskidu (A & C Black, 1975)
I'd like to each the world to sing
Going to the zoo

Ta ra ra boom de ay (A & C Black, 1977)
My Grandfather's clock
When I'm sixty-four

Songs for a Year (Rosemary Barralet Bunbury, Longmans, 1988)
I'm going to school today
Mother's Day song
Father's Day song

Silly Aunt Sally (Jan Holdstock, Ward Lock Educational, 1984)
Silly Aunt Sally
Just in case

The Family of Man (miscellaneous sources)

Science building block

AT1 L1, 2, 3
AT2 L1, 2, 3

The National curriculum Programme of Study for Key Stage 1 states that children should be finding out about themselves and should consider similarities between themselves and other children. They should also become aware of other life forms, and that this tudy should be by direct observation where appropriate.

The family life science building block focuses on observations regarding what determines belonging to and being part of a family.

SCIENCE ACTIVITIES

C24 –26

1 Prior to studying the family life science building block, invite children with pets to bring them into school. Of those who are able to do so, allocate them each to a group so that if possible each group has someone who has had experience of caring for a pet.

2 In groups, ask the children to choose a pet and list all the things their pet would need to be happy and contented. Suggest that once a pet has been chosen they should then give it a name before listing what the pet needs. Invite each group to report back to the others. The teacher should then write on the board or large sheet of paper what the children have decided.

3 Discuss with the children what it is they expect to provide for their new pet and how they would care for it on a daily basis. Consider such things as the way to handle the pets, housing, cleaning, diet, exercise, ailments and record all the answers on **copymaster 24 (Keeping my pet happy)**.

● **Note** Some children might be capable of undertaking some personal research regarding the rearing of pets and so books should be provided to support this. Able children can then act as support 'tutors' to less able children in the class. This would challenge the able children, help the less able and if dealt with in a positive and encouraging way would generally assist in the development of a caring ethos.

Our pet is called Pippin
It needs:
a hutch, vegetables,
straw/hay/sawdust,
rabbit food,
water

4 Invite children to compare what they would do to look after their chosen pet and what they need to do for themselves. Focus especially on the caring role they have towards their pet; who looks after them in such a way? Consideration will no doubt centre on the role of those who care for them at home (i.e. father, mother, brother, sister, or some other person), but there are opportunities to develop aspects of caring within the context of family life by cross-referencing other units of *Blueprints* such as Healthy eating, Keeping clean, Growing up, as well as Myself, Homes, etc. in *Blueprints Topics*.

5 Using **copymaster 25 (Animal families)** the children could be introduced to collective names for animals.

6 You may wish to finish this section by discussing with the children who does what in the family, things they can do for themselves, things they are responsible for. Use **copymaster 26 (Helping the family)** and ask the children to decide which jobs around the home they like doing and which ones they dislike. When they have completed the copymaster, encourage them to explore why they find some jobs more enjoyable than others by talking about them to their friend(s).

Mathematics building block

AT1 L1, 2, 3
AT2 L1, 3
AT3 L2, 3
AT5 L1, 2, 3

Handling data provides appropriate ways of introducing and developing in young children an understanding of the idea of growing from young to old.

MATHEMATICS ACTIVITIES

C27

1 Ask the children if they can bring to school a photograph for each year of their life. It is likely that not all children are able to do this, but as long as some are then that is enough to fulfil the required purpose.

2 Working in groups, provide children with the following:

- string with scissors
- strips of paper
- building bricks – wooden blocks or Lego®
- small objects of varying weight.

Then ask them to:

- cut string and arrange it in lengths with a long piece at one end becoming gradually shorter;
- cut strips of paper and arrange them from longest to shortest;
- build towers of bricks starting with the tallest and gradually becoming shorter;
- arrange objects of varying weights so that the heaviest is placed first and the lightest is last.

3 Using **copymaster 27 (Oldest and youngest)**, ask each child to cut out the pictures and arrange them in a line, in order of age, from oldest to youngest. Discuss with the children what criteria they used for arranging their pictures.

4 Explain to the children that in the class there are some children who are older than others and some who are younger. How do we find out exactly who is older and younger?

5 Look at the photographs that the children have brought in. Arrange them in order of age, beginning with the photograph showing them at their youngest and leading up to the present day (or as near as possible to it). Ask the children to consider the physical changes they notice and to say what they are.

6 What do they think they will look like when they are older? Comparisons might be made to their parents or other adults in the family.

7 Ask the children to find out when people in their family were born and to arrange their names along a drawn line (perhaps provided by the teacher) placing the oldest person first and then gradually working along until the youngest is placed last. It may be that certain members of the family are sensitive about their dates of birth in which case it would serve the purpose just as well to know who is older/younger.

8 Some parents, grandparents or teachers are happy to send into school photographs of themselves from when they were young to the present day. This is an excellent way of demonstrating to children the point that all people grow and change from young to old.

9 Discuss with the children the changes that occur in people as they grow older.

Geography building block

AT1 L1, 2
AT2 L1, 2, 3
AT3 L2, 3
AT4 L1, 2, 3
AT5 L1, 2, 3

Family life has a number of opportunities for exploration within a geographical context. Human geography in particular can facilitate geographical understanding and family life within a health context. Being with others is first experienced by children through the family. Leisure time enables a family to spend time together. This could be quality time for a family and the opportunities for such activities and the importance of leisure time will be addressed.

GEOGRAPHY ACTIVITIES

C28 –30

Being together

1 Ask the children to think of the times when all the family are together. Write these down on the board or a large sheet of paper.

2 When the family are able to be together, where do they go and what do they do? Replies may contain some of the following:

Grandma's, shopping, visiting friends, library, walks, bike rides, swimming pool, sports club, parties,

museum/art gallery, theatre, cinema, holidays, gardening, restaurant, hobbies, celebrations, festivals, etc.

3 When a comprehensive list has been drawn up, give each child a copy of **copymaster 28 (Being together (1))**. Ask them to match the pictures to the words by drawing a connecting line between them.

4 Now ask the children to decide which of these

tea time
going shopping
weekends
watching t.v.
taking a trip
visiting gran

activities are carried out indoors and which are done outdoors. Give each child a copy of **copymaster 29 (Being together (2))** and tell them to write 'indoors' or 'outdoors' in the spaces opposite the pictures.

Going places

1. Suggest to the class that they are going to make a guide for things to do and places to go. They will have to find out and name exactly where the places are that their family like to go. Lots of pictures will be needed and some information about the places will be required.

2. A small photocopied guide could be made and sent home to parents as a suggestion of things for the family to do.

3. As a class, talk about all the pleasant things that going places and being with the family create, and list particularly those activities thought of as being especially healthy.

4. The children might like to complete **copymaster 30 (Find the family)** by tracing the correct journey through the maze to the family in the centre.

RE building block

Not all children and their families are regular worshippers, but nearly all children should be aware of some of the major religious festivals celebrated by their friends and even themselves.

Virtually all the religious festivals are times when the celebration is a family affair. Similarly, any kind of rite of passage, be it induction into a faith, marriage or death, has a strong family involvement. A wedding is an ideal way for young children to consider how families inter-relate, celebrate ideals and values within the context of a religious ethos.

RE ACTIVITIES ▶

1. Ask the children if they know what happens when two people get married.

2. Has anyone been to a wedding? Would they like to tell the others about it? Perhaps they could bring some photographs in of the wedding. (If the teacher is married, they too could show the class photographs of their own wedding.)

3. Where do marriages take place? What religion would the people be likely to belong to if they got married in:

(a) a mosque
(b) a church
(c) a temple
(d) a gurdwara
(e) a synagogue?

4 What do people usually wear when they get married? How do people usually enjoy themselves at weddings? Why do people feel particularly happy at weddings?

It is important to point out gently to children that sometimes people no longer want to be married. For various reasons they no longer wish to be together but prefer to live apart. It is likely that the class contains children whose parents are separated or divorced. Whereas such matters no longer carry any social stigma the experience may be painful to a child. If children wish to talk about such deeply personal matters and wish to share their experiences with the class, then make it clear that there could be ground rules created such as confidentiality within the class, or that matters will be treated seriously, and as a teacher, you will not allow questions that might be considered unkind or hurtful.

Of course, not all divorces or separations are painful experiences; some children enjoy the benefit of what they see as the best of both worlds or belonging to two families. If that is the case then these feelings can also be shared. However, if a child wants to speak privately with the teacher, then his/her wishes should be respected. There is no doubt that divorce and separation is much more common these days and should not be ignored, especially within the context of family life and the different kinds of family that exist.

English building block

AT1 L1, 2, 3
AT2 L1, 2, 3
AT3 L1, 2, 3

Children tend to consider jobs that they do in the context of being helpful. Family life emphasises interdependence and the exercise of personal qualities such as reliability, tolerance, sharing, caring, kindness, honesty and perseverance. Being helpful is a way by which such qualities can be developed and the family, as in the close personal family within the home, or the class 'family' at school, is the context.

ENGLISH ACTIVITIES

1 Discuss with the children the people in school who help us. Point out that the children themselves also have a part to play in helping around the school. Make a list of all the jobs that children do in the classroom and around the school:

Picking up litter, taking dinner money to the secretary, taking messages, washing paint pots/brushes, giving out paper, helping tie laces, tidying book shelves, etc.

2 Consider what might make a teacher choose a particular pupil to do a job for her/him. List the qualities a teacher might expect of a person who does a job for her/him.

3 List the reasons why anyone in the class should want to do a job.

4 Discuss what kind of jobs are done in and around the house. Are there jobs that a mother usually does and jobs that a father usually does? Can any of these jobs be done by either? (There is an obvious opportunity here to consider gender roles and stereotyping.)

5 Hand out copies of **copymaster 31 (Jobs at home)** and ask the children to identify the member of the family performing each task.

6 Returning to **copymaster 26 (Helping the family)** and related work (see p. 28), ask the class to conduct a survey of jobs done at home. Information could be gathered to answer the following questions:

- which jobs are performed by the most children?
- which are (a) the most popular and (b) the most unpopular tasks?
- what reasons are given as to why some jobs are more enjoyable than others?
- how do these jobs help those who care for us?

7 Ask the children to draw a picture showing themselves doing a job in school and to write underneath the picture saying why they like doing the job. Display the work in categories according to the job chosen. The display could be in the form of a blockgraph.

Love

1 Discuss the reasons why the children like/love the person who cares for them. What does 'love' mean? Are there different kinds of love? Is love of your pet the same as loving your Mum?

2 On a large sheet of paper or on the board, write the qualities that the children describe.

3 Ask the children to write a story about, or describe, the person they really love and give the reasons why. It might be a good idea to mount the work carefully on card, decorate the borders and present it to the person it is written about. This would make the point that sometimes it is better to declare our feelings rather than keep them to ourselves – and how good it is to be complimented.

ASSESSMENT

Open-ended techniques of assessment can be very revealing in helping teachers and children to recognise the learning that has taken place.

1 Give each child a copy of **copymaster 32 (Caring for each other)**.

2 Ask the children to draw a picture or write a word in each round balloon to show that they know what their family does for them.

3 In the heart shaped balloons, the children should write a word that tells what they do for their family.

BEING SAFE

Building blocks of the curriculum

Citizenship

- Responsibility a citizen has towards him/herself and others

Art

- Colour
- Shape
- Pattern

Science

- Conspicuity
- Senses
- Floating and sinking

Environment

- Recognising quality and vulnerability of different environments
- Promoting positive attitudes towards a pupil's own environment

History

- Time: now and then
- Pupil's own history
- Events in pupil's lives
- Use of artefacts and pictures

Mathematics

- Shape
- Pattern
- Sorting
- Handling data
- Speed/distance

Economic and industrial awareness

- Marketing safety products

Geography

- Introduction to basic map work
- Urban/rural trail
- Home-school routes

English

- Descriptive writing
- Imaginative writing
- Vocabulary
- Reading
- Speaking, listening, drama

Music

- Different sounds
- Composition
- Improvisation

PE

- Controlling movement
- Co-operative and supportive role in team work

RE

- Three leading religions
- Stories concerned with caring and responsibility

Technology

- Problem solving
- Identifying needs
- Designing
- Materials
- Construction

INTRODUCTION

Each year some 200 children die in accidents around the home and the garden (Aucott, 1990). Figures for 1988 released by the Department of Transport show that 462 children aged up to 15 were killed in road accidents and another 8,909 were seriously injured. This reason alone is ample justification for safety education, which the National Curriculum Council has rightly acknowledged as an important part of the school curriculum.

Wherever children are, in the home, at school, in the locality, near water or roads, an element of personal danger can be found. It is not only from accidents that a child is at risk. Ill-intentioned people, adults and youngsters, may wish children harm. **Being safe** is about enabling children to avoid situations which place them at risk.

Curriculum Guidance 5 learning objectives

Pupils should:

- know the potential dangers in different environments, e.g. road, water, home.
- develop and be able to practise simple ways of keeping safe and finding help.
- know about personal safety, e.g. know that individuals have rights over their own bodies and there are differences between good and bad touches; begin to develop simple skills and practices which will help maintain personal safety.

STARTING POINTS

- Read the children the story of 'I'm Going to Get You' or 'Little Red Riding Hood' (both by Tony Ross, Andersen Press). Discuss the story with them, noting the danger and risk elements in the story.

- Invite the children to draw or write a sentence about things that frighten them. Ask them how they feel when they are frightened. You may wish to write these words up on the board.

- Ask the children who they go to when they don't feel safe; when they are frightened. Who makes them feel safe? Write down their suggestions on the board or some large sheets of paper.

- Ask the children where they think they need to be safe. Write down their suggestions as above.

- Display the suggestions around the classroom and tell the children they are going to find out about being safe.

What frightens us?
dogs thunder
strangers
crossing the road the sea

Who makes us feel safe?
mum dad
crossing lady
my sister
my pet dog

Where do we feel safe?
home
nan's bed
school

Feelings
sick
worried
sad
crying

Where we need to be safe
· in the park
· with fireworks
· climbing trees
· crossing the road
· in the kitchen
· by a river

Science building block

AT1 L1, 2, 3
AT2 L1, 2, 3
AT3 L1, 2, 3
AT4 L1, 2, 3

There are many opportunities to explore safety issues through Science activities. Key Stage 1 suggests that Science activities should allow children to: appreciate the need for safe and careful action; take responsibility for living things, know about their needs and understand the care required; know about personal safety; experience forces, e.g. road safety activities; understand the danger and misuse of electricity.

SCIENCE ACTIVITIES

C33
–35

Conspicuity

1 You will need assorted coloured paper (gummed paper is preferable) and a sheet of black paper for each child. Place the coloured paper in a pile on the desks of each group of children. Ask them to sort the colours into bright colours and dull colours.

2 Then ask the children to make a picture using the black paper as a background and the dull colours for objects. One object only should be created from bright colours. Display these at the back of the class. Ask the children to name each bright object in the picture and to record which colour was the most visible and which was the least. Discuss why the object was more visible and what lessons this might have for people out walking.

3 Introduce the class to fluorescent colours (these can be bought from stationers in the form of card or labels used by shopkeepers for pricing). Use the fluorescent card/labels to create an object and place this on either the picture made from gummed paper or make a new picture. Although the fluorescent object will obviously stand out, the observation can be enhanced by asking children to wear sunglasses and look at the pictures.

4 Ask the children where they have seen fluorescent colours used. For example: fire engines, police cars, ambulances and crossing patrols. The children could make a mobile of vehicles with fluorescent letters and people; some with bright clothes and some with dull clothes.

5 Ask the children to construct a class graph noting the colours of each child's clothes. Say who is wearing 'safe' clothes. What is meant by safe? Emphasise the importance of wearing colours that enable people to be

seen, especially by motorists, and mention strips/armbands worn over outdoor clothing in the dark.

clothes	red	blue	yellow	white	black	brown	safe	unsafe
coat					✓			✓
jumper			✓				✓	
blouse				✓			✓	

6 Children should understand that it is not only the wearing of bright colours that helps motorists to see people walking near to or across roads. Being seen means giving road users plenty of time to adjust to people crossing. Ask the children to give examples of what might attract children to run out on to the road and use these to form a set of rules.

> When near the road **DON'T** run out for your runaway ball!
>
> When near the road **DON'T** run out to the ice-cream van!
>
> When near the road **DON'T** run to see your friend!
>
> When near the road **DON'T** run out from between parked cars!
>
> When near the road **DON'T** leave a grown-up's side!

Children might want to make posters of these for display around the school.

Senses

You may wish to introduce this aspect of safety by undertaking some of the simple experiments in *Blueprints Topics*, page 4, to help the children identify and discuss their senses. Knowing about and being able to use our five senses is very important for being safe.

Touch

1 Using mail-order catalogues and working in groups, ask the children to select and group pictures of electrical items, cutlery, pans, cookers, gas fires. Discuss with the children things they should not touch and why and when they should not touch them.

2 Look around the classroom and see what could be dangerous if touched: electric sockets, hot radiators, scissors, glass jam-jars if cracked or broken, compasses, anything broken such as a desk hinge, an unguarded guillotine (assuming a safety guard is fitted, discuss why).

3 Now complete **copymaster 33 (All around the house)**. The children indicate dangerous items by colouring the square accompanying the picture red, and safe items by colouring the square green.

Smell and taste

1 The smell and taste of unfamiliar substances provides an opportunity to indulge in playing with words by having fun inventing new words. Carry out a simple wordplay exercise by asking the children to describe the taste/smell of selected items:

Taste	Smell
lemon	onion
honey	perfume
coffee	cheese
peppermint	sour milk

2 Discuss with the children why they should never taste or smell things in bottles, jars, packets or tins that they don't know the origin of or are especially strange to them. What might be in them? Write down suggestions, e.g. poison, medicine, cleaning fluid, etc.

3 Using **copymaster 34 (Monster!)**, tell the children to draw a monster coming out of the bottle. The children could be asked to repeat the activity on a larger scale.

4 Fire! Fire! ... What should children do if they smell burning either at home or in school? Discuss with children how to make an emergency call. (Old telephones or toy telephones are usually easy to obtain.) Inform children of what to do in the event of discovering a fire in the school. Take the children through a fire drill.

Looking and listening

1 Ask the children to select a child and then blindfold the nominee. Ensuring that no harm comes to them, ask the child to walk to a chosen cupboard in the class-room. Lack of vision should prove very difficult for the easy completion of the task. Several children can take part.

2 Then ask the children in which situation they should look carefully to be safe. Discuss the Green Cross Code with them. Relate looking to conspicuity.

3 Stress how important listening is for being safe. Using percussion instruments, arrange a group of children to make the sounds of traffic. When the 'music' (a good sounding cacophony) stops the children can move freely around the hall or classroom. When the 'music' starts all the children must stop. This can be played as a game similar to musical statues. Those who move when they should be still are eliminated.

4 Set up a table in the classroom with a collection of things which the children have suggested should not be touched, smelled or tasted. Label them.

5 The children can complete the crossword puzzle on **copymaster 35 (Senses crossword)**.

Floating and sinking
This aspect of being safe could be supported by the topic on water, and floating and sinking in particular on page 60 of *Blueprints Topics*.

1 Ask the children to collect different examples of materials found around them, e.g. wood, metal, cork, glass, marble, plastic beads, a small bottle/cannister, sponge, cloth (you may wish to provide these). Discuss with them which materials they think will float and which will sink. Ask them to draw a chart and to place each object or material under the appropriate column of either 'floats' or 'sinks'.

Floats	Sinks
WOOD	GLASS

2 Provide enough water-troughs for the children to work in small groups so that they can test their hypotheses. Ask the children to test each different object or material by putting it in the water. Tell them to record whether or not it floats or sinks.

3 Discuss with the children which objects floated. Were these the same as the objects they predicted? Discuss the qualities of things that float, e.g. lightness, containing air, a skin that doesn't absorb water – as opposed to things that sink.

SAUCEPANS   IRONS   SHARP KNIVES   BROKEN GLASS   MEDICINES   DRINKS   KETTLES

Things we must not touch, smell or taste

4 Discuss with the children why playing near water can be dangerous.

5 Bring to their attention that even people who work at sea take great care over their safety. Ask what do people who work on ships or sail boats wear that helps to keep them afloat if the boat sinks. Sometimes objects can be heavy but still float (children enjoy meeting new words so it would not be inappropriate to introduce the word 'buoyancy'). Why was this? (Clue: air)

What colour are life jackets? Why are they fluorescent pink, yellow or orange? (Make a link to work on conspicuity here.)

Review with the children things they have worked on and learned through the **Being safe** Science activities.

Mathematics building block

AT1 L1, 2, 3
AT4 L1, 2, 3
AT5 L1, 2, 3

The significance of shape and pattern in keeping people safe.
A combination of colour, shape and pattern is commonly used as a means of informing and warning people of their personal safety. Road signs are a particular example of this. Estimating with some degree of accuracy is also an important safety skill for children to acquire and which can be taught and developed through Mathematics.

MATHEMATICS ACTIVITIES

1 Divide the class into groups of four or five children. Using either gummed paper or tissue in shapes of circles, squares, ovals, triangles and rectangles, ask the children to:

(a) estimate how many of each shape there might be;
(b) arrange the shapes in different patterns and sequences;
(c) sort the shapes into colours;

(d) sort them into groups according to shape.

Children can be introduced to a variety of mathematical exercises in relation to shapes (these can incorporate 2- and 3-D shapes for older pupils).

2 Ask the children to list where they have seen these shapes in the particular colours. Suggest they may create a picture using the different shapes.

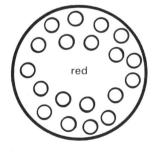

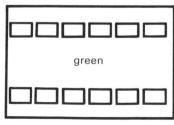

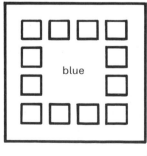

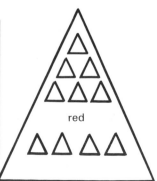

3 Some shapes and colours help to keep us safe on the roads. Ask the children to colour and label the shapes on **copymaster 36 (Shapes)**. The shapes can be cut out and stuck, according to shape/colour, on to a large sheet of paper, itself cut to the shape being represented.

4 On the road, shapes help keep us safe because ...

- **blue circles** tell us **to do something**.
- **red circles** tell us **not to do something**.

- **red triangles** give us **warnings**.
- **blue rectangles** give **information**.
- **green rectangles** give **directions**.

5 Using all the shapes and colours, create a set of signs for use around the class or school.

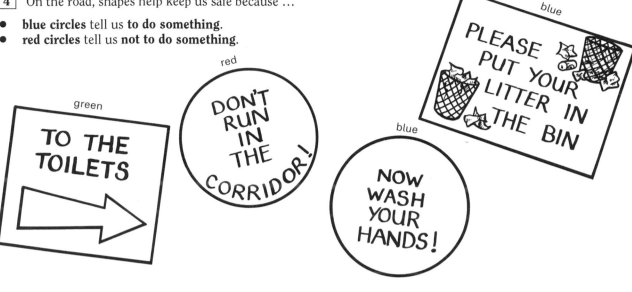

English building block

AT1 L1, 2, 3
AT2 L1, 2, 3
AT3 L1, 2, 3
AT4 L1, 2, 3
AT5 L1, 2, 3

Children need the opportunity to express their feelings of trust, friendship, safety, fears and doubts. Without knowing how they feel or what their thoughts are it is impossible to gauge what they need to know regarding their personal safety. English is the key to unlocking their innermost thoughts and feelings.

ENGLISH ACTIVITIES

This area of work requires great sensitivity on the part of the teacher. Some children may speak openly about their feelings. This can sometimes result in the school having to decide whether further action in the form of counselling or involvement of specialist agencies needs to be sought. Often it is enough to guarantee confidentiality in the form of 'ground rules'.

1 Read the class the story of 'Little Red Riding Hood' (the Tony Ross version is excellent for the purpose of considering being safe). Ask the children how they think Little Red Riding Hood must have felt when she began to realise who might be under the sheets. Write their

ideas down on the board or a large sheet of paper. Remind them of the things that frightened them and how they felt (see **Starting points**).

2 **Copymaster 37 (Little Red Riding Hood)** depicts Red Riding Hood in a number of situations. Ask the children to assess how safe she is in each. The borders can then be coloured in red to show that each situation is potentially dangerous.

3 Ask the children what the wolf did in order to get close to Little Red Riding Hood. Then ask the children

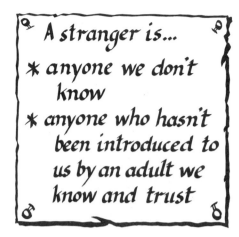

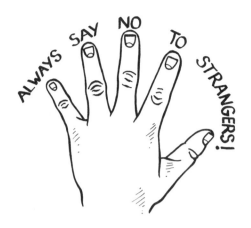

who they need to be wary of. If the word 'stranger' has not already appeared on the large sheet of paper/board suggest to the children that we should include it. Discuss what a stranger is. Write down all their ideas.

4   Ask the children what a stranger may look like; emphasise that a stranger can look just like Mummy/ Daddy/the person who looks after us. Allow the class to say what a stranger might say to you or ask you to do. Write these down on a big sheet of paper/board.

5   What might strangers do? Write the children's ideas down on the board/large sheet of paper.

> A stranger might...
> * offer to buy me sweets
> * say mummy has asked him to collect me from school
> * ask me to help him look for his dog
> * offer me a ride in his car
> * touch me

6   The focus on strangers might be undertaken through role-play. Working in groups or pairs children/a child can play the part of the stranger(s) and make an approach.

7   Now develop this further by asking the children what they should do if they are approached in this way. Using their ideas, suggest they should always say 'NO' and they should always tell an adult they know and trust as soon as they are able. A simple rhyme like the one below might help children to remember.

> Remember the rule of fingers and thumb
> Whenever a stranger asks you to come:
> ALWAYS SAY NO TO STRANGERS!

Some children might want to make their own rhyme up.

8   With the children in pairs; one child should play the part of the stranger and make approaches similar to those suggested, and the other should practise saying 'No, go away!'.

9   Ask the children who can help us if we don't feel safe.

> People who can help us:
> policeman
> crossing lady/man
> neighbour shopkeeper
> teacher
> dinner lady
> caretaker

10   Remind children that not all strangers mean to trick us or harm us. Suggest to them that they should always say 'no' to anyone, including people they know, if they don't feel safe, or if someone touches them in a way they don't like/gives them a bad feeling.

11   Now ask the children about things that make them feel good/happy. Allow them to sit in a large circle and ask each child in turn to complete the sentence:

   'I feel good/happy when ....

Don't allow the other children to interrupt, suggesting that they listen very carefully to what each person says.

12   Some children may want to write about their feelings. The following exercise will help to focus on the language of feelings. Make word-boxes with words associated with feeling safe, feeling sad, feeling afraid,

feeling happy. (Particularly young children could make drawings of faces and place them in a box; the words could be written by the teacher. Older pupils could use the words to write stories or poems about feelings.)

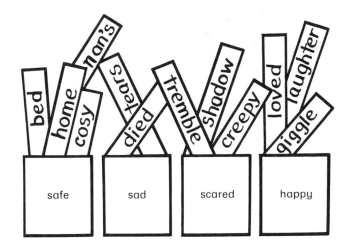

Music/Technology building block

> AT1 L1, 2, 3
> AT2 L1, 2, 3
> AT3 L1, 2, 3
> AT4 L1, 2, 3

Sounds play an important part in keeping people safe. Warning sounds have a particular identity and can be produced through instruments and objects, machines, the human voice and through animals and creatures in nature. Music is a challenging way for children to study sound in relation to warnings, but it is important for children to be able not only to identify warning sounds but also be able to respond to them.

It is important for children to consider the difficulties presented to people who are deaf and are unable to be warned of danger by means of sound.

MUSIC/TECHNOLOGY ACTIVITIES

1 Ask the class if they can think of different sounds that give warnings. Suggest that they can be made by creatures or by people.

2 Using **copymaster 38 (Warning sounds)**, tell the children to match the sounds shown in the left-hand column to the situations in the right-hand column by drawing a connecting line.

3 Tell the story of the Roman soldiers who were defending their town and were saved from a surprise attack by a warning given by geese and ask the children to make up a scenario involving an animal giving a warning. For example, a dog asleep in her master's home … (intruder, fire, sickness, etc.)

4 What things do sounds warn us about and in so doing help to keep us safe? Give an example: a Pelican crossing 'bleep' tells us it is safe to cross the road.

5 What is it about a noise that tells us that it might

41

Dog barking Police siren
Smoke detector Fog horn
Monkey screeching Car horn
Burglar alarm Lion roaring
Blackbird chirping
Pelican crossing
Alarm clock

ACME ALARM

TWEET TWEET

BLAH!

be a warning noise? (shrill sound, loud blast, short and sharp, intermittent, deep bellow, etc.)

6 Give the children a range of musical instruments divided into the following categories.

- Instruments made to be hit or shaken: drums, maracas, cymbals, triangles, bongoes, piano, xylophone, tambour, glockenspiel, chimebars.
- Instruments made to be scraped: guiro, cello, violin.
- Instruments made to be plucked: banjo, guitar, harp, autoharp, sitar, mandolin.
- Instruments made to be blown: penny whistle, flute, clarinet, oboe, trumpet, harmonica, recorder, bamboo pipe.

It is likely that a school will only have some of these instruments, but try to assemble something of what you can in each category. Explain to the children the different categories to which each belongs. Ask them to make their own warning sounds based on signals they have heard, using one or more of the instruments.

7 From a range of scrap materials such as cocoa tins, elastic bands, boxes, paper, combs, etc., previously gathered from home, ask the children to make their own 'instrument'. Then (a) see if they can place them in any of the named categories; (b) ask the children to create a warning sound using their home-made instrument.

8 In small groups of about four, encourage the children to create a short role-play about being safe using the musical sounds to communicate warnings at appropriate places. Some groups could represent animals, some could represent people/machines. Allow each group three or four minutes to present their play. (Remember that role-play should not be competitive or violent.)

Ask the children what they learned from their friends' plays.

Geography building block

| AT1 L1, 2, 3 |
| AT2 L1, 2 |
| AT4 L1 |
| AT5 L1, 2, 3 |

Finding safe places to play.

If a child is taken away from their own locality and placed in unfamiliar surroundings one of their first reactions is that of feeling unsafe. Through geography it is possible for the child to have a sense of identification with, and knowledge of, their surroundings that should lead to a secure feeling and safe use of the environment.

GEOGRAPHY ACTIVITIES

C39 –41

1 Working in pairs, ask the children to describe their route to school to each other. Tell them to note which roads they have to cross, who helps them to cross the road, and to say which landmarks there are along the way, e.g. newspaper shop, bridge, postbox, zebra-crossing, etc.

2 Ask some of the children to describe their route(s) to school. Choose children who have particularly interesting journeys or those whose journey involves a certain risk. Some children will come to school by car. If they can't remember the journey ask them to make notes of their journey the next time they come to school. It would be an appropriate time to talk about the need to be a good passenger and all that that entails.

3 For young children, an important aid to being safe is knowing their address and telephone number. Make sure each child knows these details which can be recorded on **copymaster 39 (Where do I live?)**. The labels could be coloured, cut out and mounted to form a classroom display.

4 Ask the children to say where they think they have to be very careful when they travel to school.

5 Show the class a map of their locality (a photocopy of an A–Z map would do adequately). Ask them what they can tell you about the map. If a child doesn't bring to your attention the grid lines then point to them yourself. Explain how grid lines help us to find something on a map. Use **copymaster 40 (Co-ordinates)** to enable children to understand the use of grid lines. Relate this exercise to similar work in the **Medicines and drugs** unit (see p. 8).

6 Discuss safe places to cross roads. Suggest that the local council would like to put certain signs or notices at these places warning people to take care. What might

these signs look like? What might they say? What about people who cannot read English?

7 Imagine that a new child has come to the neighbourhood and is looking for the best place to play in the locality. Where do the children recommend? Is the best place the safest place? What is meant by the 'best' place? What might make a play area unsafe? (Remind the children that they should always let Mummy or Daddy or the person who looks after them, know where they are.)

8 Using **copymaster 41 (Journey to school)**, suggest that the children play the game in pairs or fours. You will need dice or spinners and some counters. Each player takes turns to make their way from home to school; the player who arrives at school first is the winner. Before starting the game, write on a large piece of paper or on the board some 'golden rules' for a safe journey to school.

> Always go straight to school
>
> Never talk to strangers
> Cross roads at safe place
> Never play near railways or water

History building block

AT1 L1, 2, 3
AT2 L3
AT3 L1, 2, 3

People can learn from the experiences of the past. The consequences of what has previously taken place can be taken into account; this is especially true in relation to personal and public safety. Through a comparative approach it is possible for children to consider the actions of the past compared to those of today. How much safer are we in our daily lives today than in the past?

HISTORY ACTIVITIES

Our homes

1 Discuss with the children what houses were like a

long time ago. (You might have previously put pictures of houses from the past in the classroom.)

2 Ask the children how they think the houses were heated and lit. Where did water for drinking come from? Did they have toilets?

3 Ask the children to sort out the pictures on **copymaster 42 (Past and present)** into those items found in modern houses and those found in houses a long time ago. Corresponding numbers should be written in the right-hand column.

4 What might have been considered a danger in these houses of long ago?

Our health

1 Ask the children if they think that people were generally healthy years ago. What sort of things might have made people ill and unsafe? Compare those sources of danger and poor hygiene (as indicated through inferior housing and hygiene facilities) with today's homes.

2 Ask the children what illnesses they have had (give some ideas, such as measles, chickenpox, flu, etc.). Ask what they can do to keep themselves healthy.

3 Who looks after our health? Ask the children to make a list or draw a picture of all those people who look

after our health from when we are babies. Talk about why it is important for everyone to have vaccinations against diseases.

Lights

1 Compare lighting in the past with the lighting we have today. A source of lighting a long time ago was candlelight and lanterns. Both could be considered dangerous if not closely watched.

2 Make lanterns using coloured paper or card. Follow the simple design below, which can be varied and enhanced, perhaps by examining lanterns from other countries and different periods in history.

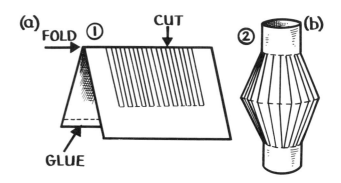

RE building block

Caring, responsibility and love that one individual has for another in order to ensure their safety.

The great religions of the world have a universal approach to the well-being of a person. At the centre of such a concept is the caring, love and responsibility one person should have for his or her fellow being.

RE ACTIVITIES

1 Tell one of the following stories: The good Samaritan; Muhammed's flight from Mecca; Guru Gobind Singh and the water carrier (from *Assembly Stories from Around the World*, W. Dargue, OUP). Draw parallels between these stories and some things the children themselves could do to show similar qualities.

2 Working together as a class, draw up a children's charter regarding caring for others. Consider the proposals in the context of being and feeling safe.

3 Invite a local church, temple or mosque leader to the school in order to talk to the class about their work, emphasising the caring aspects of a spiritual leader's job.

4 Ask the children to keep a diary recording those actions that were considerate and those that were

selfish. Consider how selfish behaviour can lead to unsafe actions and feelings.

Caring for others
Be nice to each other
Share things
Listen to each other
Don't be spiteful
Help each other

Class 2.

PE building block

In order to be safe, the children need control and co-ordination of their movement. this can be practised through the safe use of apparatus, co-operative and individual physical activities in PE.

PE ACTIVITIES

It is standard practice for teachers to stress all aspects of safety during PE. The following are suggestions for particularly emphasising the importance of being safe.

1 In the playground or school hall, ask the children to find a space and, on command, run in different directions taking great care not to bump into each other and to be safe. Tell them that on the whistle or command they should stop instantly and become statues. Repeat this several times, telling them to run fast or slowly and change the activity from running to hopping, jumping, running backwards, bunny hopping, etc.

2 Similarly, have the children running into space but on command they should form groups of different sizes (groups of three, five, sixteen, etc.) and make 'safe shapes' e.g. lifting and supporting each other, rolling up, or balancing.

3 Using apparatus, emphasise balancing activities and the safe use of equipment and apparatus, both in and out of school.

- **Note** Technology and Art have not been addressed as independent blocks but are incorporated as aspects of other blocks within this unit.

ASSESSMENT

Rules for Being Safe
1. Cross the road at the Pelican
2. Don't play near water
3. Let mummy know where you are playing
4. Don't talk to strangers
5. Don't play with sharp things
6. etc. etc.
Signed
   Class 2

It is important that children can recognise the things that they can do to keep themselves safe. Self-assessment is a significant part of the learning process.

1 As a class activity discuss with the children anything that they can remember about being safe. Pay particular attention to reinforcing the skills for being safe in each of the different contexts.

2 Ask the children to complete the self-assessment sheet **copymaster 43 (Keeping safe)** by drawing a smiling face in the circle if they think they can do those things shown all/most of the time.

3 Tell them to keep the sheet safe and fill in any blanks they can when they are able to in the future.

4 As a class activity, write a list of rules for being safe and turn them into a 'charter' which can be displayed in the classroom or school hall. A piece of flip chart paper or larger would be the appropriate size. Make the charter appear to be 'ancient' by snipping the edges, browning the paper and attaching a ribbon.

EXERCISING

Building blocks of the curriculum

Citizenship

- Working together and valuing everyone's contribution
- The Olympic ideal
- Winning and losing

PE

- The benefits of aerobic exercise

Science

- Machines, fuel and energy

Environment

- What counts as an exercise – where does it take place?

Art

- Designing flags

Mathematics

- Introduction to time
- How long it takes to …
- How many can be done by …

History

- Sports of long ago – the ancient Greeks

Economic and industrial awareness

- Machines and fuel

Geography

- 'International sports'
- Flags of different countries

English

- Rudiments of story writing

Technology

- Designing a machine to keep us healthy

Music

- Music to dance and move to; improvising, traditional and folk
- Action songs

RE

- Teamwork – working together

INTRODUCTION

In a report of the Royal College of Physicians (1991) it was made clear that the 'benefits of exercise for everyone, young and old, far outweighed the hazards for everyone'.

This is certainly not a new concept. As long ago as 1909, The Syllabus of Physical Exercises for Schools (HMSO, 1909) recognised the 'ability of physical training to raise the child's power to resist the onset of disease'. Most recently, research undertaken at Exeter University has shown that primary school aged children are generally overweight and under-exercised and are in danger of developing coronary heart disease in later life as a result (Armstrong, 1990). Besides eating more carefully, the recommendation is that children should exercise more often and should certainly undertake aerobic exercise for at least twenty minutes three times a week. Moreover, there is some evidence to suggest that, besides health benefits, children who exercise regularly are more likely to have a more positive sense of well being and raised self-esteem (Dowling, 1986).

However, simply repeating physical activities and exercises over a period of time is not enough; activities need to be fun and enjoyable if children, through choice, are to continue exercising. Increasing the competitive nature of physical exercise is not the answer. This will serve only to 'turn off' many young people as they grow and develop through adolescence. The health benefits of exercise are immeasurable: the sooner children begin regular exercise which is enjoyable and in which they have some involvement and control, then the hope is that they will continue as Williams (1987) suggests, 'to be interested and participate in later life'.

Curriculum Guidance 5 learning objectives

Pupils should:

- know that people feel better when they take regular exercise.
- know that exercise uses energy that comes from food.

STARTING POINTS

C44 –45

- Tell the children to complete **copymaster 44 (Exercising)** by drawing a smiling face against the activities which they think exercise them most.

- Ask the class why they think that exercise is good for us. What benefits are there? What is exercise?

- Discuss with the class whether they think that all people can exercise – which people cannot? (If they think that people with a physical disability can't, then use this as a means of talking about disabled sportsmen and women.) Is there an age limit to exercise?

- Ask the children which activities, involving exercise, they participate in. Remind them that it doesn't have to be sport; that walking the dog or playing tig count as exercise also. Write down their ideas and display them, or ask them to draw/paint a picture of the activity they do.

- Ask them how they feel when they have done these: hot, tired, sweaty, good, etc.

- Make a classroom display of clothes and equipment associated with different exercise and sports' activities. Suggest that the children bring in materials if appropriate.

- The children may also like to play the **Snakes and ladders** game on **copymaster 45** which relates to exercise. Divide the class into groups of four and provide each with dice and counters. When they have finished tell the children that they are going to do some work all about the importance of exercise.

dancing gym club swimming

walking the dog   football

riding   'tig'   running

playing catch   hopscotch

Science building block

AT1 L1, 2, 3
AT2 L2, 3
AT3 L1, 2, 3
AT4 L1, 2, 3

Machines, fuel and energy.

SCIENCE ACTIVITIES

C46

1 Using magazines, catalogues and books from the library, ask the children, working in groups of three or four, to find as many different machines as they can. Suggest that they make collages of machines cut from the magazines, etc.

2 Discuss with the children what the different machines are used for. Ask them what makes the machines go. Suggest they all need fuel to make them work, be it petrol, diesel, electricity, etc. Inform the children that we too are like machines and that we need 'energy' to make us work.

3 Ask the children what fuel gives us our energy to make us work.

4 The children can complete **copymaster 46 (Fuel)**.

They can also bring in models/toys of machines to make a classroom display.

5 Invite the children to discuss what types of food they need to help them grow and to give them the energy they need. Remind them that for the human machine to work properly it needs different foods.

6 Ask them what happens to machines when they are working (i.e. they get hot!) What do some machines produce which isn't very pleasant? Noise and smoke! Ask the children what name we give to this. (Cross-reference to pollution in **The environment** p. 84.)

7 Ask the children what the waste-products from human machines are. Remind them that they should always wash their hands after going to the toilet and before handling food.

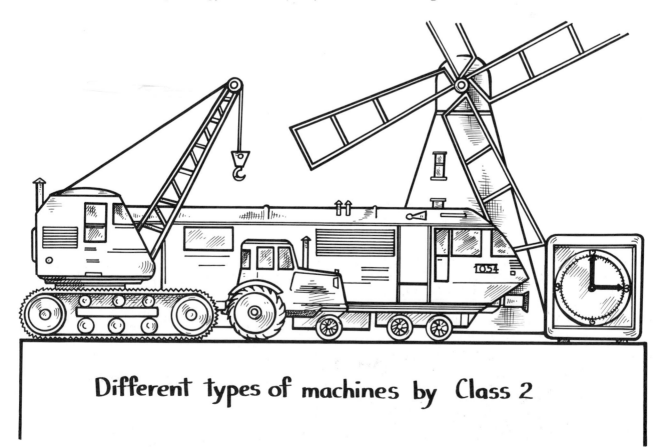

Different types of machines by Class 2

Technology building block

```
AT1 L1, 2, 3
AT2 L1, 2, 3
AT3 L1, 2, 3
AT4 L1, 2, 3
```

Technology in the form of devices and machinery plays an increasingly common part in personal exercise and fitness. Each machine, or part of it, is designed to develop efficiency of a particular part of the body. This building block offers the opportunity to undertake all four Attainment Targets of Technology in the National Curriculum.

TECHNOLOGY ACTIVITIES

C47 –48

1 Using the collages created in the Science building block (p. 50) as the starting point, discuss with the children the different types of machines they are aware of.

2 Challenge them to think of any 'machines' that some people use to keep them healthy. Write down their suggestions. (As this might be difficult for them, have some prepared pictures from magazine advertisements ready to show them.)

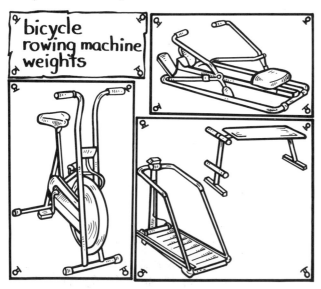

bicycle
rowing machine
weights

3 Using **copymaster 47 (Machines)**, ask the children to design a machine that could keep us healthy in some way by making us exercise. Remind them of the activities they do for exercise – can they invent a

machine that would help them do this? (Look at exercise 'machines' that hamsters and pet mice have in their cages.)

4 Making use of household junk suggest to the children that they make models of their machines and write a sentence to explain how their machines would

Models of machines to keep us healthy

be good for them. Display the machine designs and models in the classroom.

5 Ask the children if they think their machines would really work. Discuss with them the importance of regular exercise to help keep them healthy and that machines cannot exercise for us.

6 The children could complete the **Wordsearch** on **copymaster 48** to help them with their vocabulary.

Music building block

Dance has an important contribution to make to exercise and being healthy.

MUSIC ACTIVITIES

Free expression

1 Select a range of music that varies in style, tempo and mood. Choose pieces of music that are fast/slow, happy/sad, loud/quiet. Choose music from different cultures/parts of the world.

2 Play these pieces of music to the children and then ask them what sort of actions they could do in time to it. Is it music to stretch to, jump to, is it galloping music, etc.?

3 Play the music again and ask the children to move according to how they feel the music is taking them. Reinforce the action part of the music verbally, e.g. running, jumping, stretching, etc.

At the end of each piece ask the children how they feel.

Folk dancing

1 You may wish to follow this up by looking at different forms of dancing from around the world. Maypole dancing can be a very effective way of improving concentration, team work and responsibility besides being fun and good exercise.

2 If you have children from other cultures in your class, suggest that they demonstrate their particular 'folk' dance by bringing in the appropriate music on tape. Spanish Flamenco, Asian Bangra and Irish Reels can provide rich sources of study as well as exercise.

3 It is possible to invite dancers from your local Arts Centre or Community Groups to demonstrate dance and to work with children.

Action songs

1 There are many action songs which are available for children to participate in with or without music. Many of these can be found in the music and song books currently available. Some examples are:

- Head, shoulders, knees and toes
- Hokey cokey
- The wheels on the bus
- One finger one thumb.

- **Note** The important message throughout to children is that exercise can be fun, that it doesn't have to be about sport, and dance is a good way of having fun and exercising.

English building block

AT1 L1, 2, 3	Producing independently pieces
AT2 L1, 2, 3	of writing using complete
AT3 L1, 2, 3	sentences and structuring
AT4 L1, 2, 3	sentences of real or imagined
AT5 L1, 2, 3	events are important stages in
	developing the rudiments of
	story structure.

ENGLISH ACTIVITIES

1 Speaking to all the class, tell the children that people feel better when they take regular exercise. After exercise people might say: 'It's fun!', 'It's lovely!'; or they might say: 'It makes me ...' Think of all the things people might say after exercise to show they like it.

2 Make a list on the board or a large sheet of paper recording what the children tell you. They might say:

- it makes me happy
- it makes me laugh
- it makes me giggle
- it makes me smile
- it makes me feel good
- it makes me feel well.

3 Remind the children of all the different kinds of exercise they take. Make a note of the things they do. Children could draw a simple picture to illustrate each one.

walking the dog
playing tig
gardening
swimming
aerobics
riding bike
P.E.
disco dancing

4 Ask the children to choose four (or more) kinds of exercise and say/write how they might feel when they

exercise. Tell them to choose from the ideas they have already given and which are on the board. Give an example:

Playing tig makes me giggle.

5 Using the examples of different kinds of exercise already mentioned by the children think of three simple sentences for each one and ask the children to sort the sentences into a proper order. Give an example:

I find a friend. It makes us giggle. We play tig.
I find a friend. We play tig. It makes us giggle.

6 **Copymaster 49 (Sequencing)** can be used to develop this exercise. Ask the children to read the sentences and write them in the order they think they should be in the spaces provided.

Mathematics building block

AT1 L1, 2, 3
AT2 L1, 2, 3
AT3 L1, 2
AT4 L1, 2
AT5 L1, 2, 3

Activities that focus on exercise offer children opportunities to use and apply Mathematics (81). This building block introduces the concept of time and invites children to compare individual performances.

MATHEMATICS ACTIVITIES

You will need a stopwatch and a large clock face showing markings in minutes/seconds and a single hand.

1 Discuss with the class what they think 'time' is. (The general discussion will probably focus on 'how long it takes to do something'.)

2 Ask the class if any of them know how time is measured? Can they give any examples? Ask them to fill in **copymaster 50 (Times)**: times of 'daily events' can be written in each circle. Additional circles can be drawn if necessary.

It may be that although some children have heard of things happening at certain times of the day, they may not necessarily understand how time is actually measured. Establish that time is measured in units of seconds, minutes, hours, days, weeks and months without going into detail.

3 Ask the children what is the smallest amount (unit) of time they think can be measured. By using the clock face, demonstrate that a second is a very small amount of time and that there are sixty seconds in one minute, which is the time it takes for the (second) hand of the clock to go once right the way round.

4 Show them the stopwatch and explain how it works, explain its accuracy and give a demonstration inviting the children to try it out for themselves.

5 In the school hall (although it is possible for some activities to take place in the classroom or the playground), explain to the children that they are going to do a number of different things, some with apparatus and some without. Tell them that, using the stopwatch, you will time each activity and from the time you say go until the time you say stop will be exactly one minute. A

friend/partner will count how much each child is able to do in that one minute and will write it down for them on a piece of paper. Then they will swop round and do the same for their friend/partner.

6 With the children in pairs arrange for the following activities to take place:

- skipping
- hopping on one foot
- hoola-hoop around the waist
- bench-mat 'circuit' (balancing along up-turned bench, followed by forward-roll and back to start)
- throwing bean bags into a bucket some distance away
- retrieve as many rubber rings as possible from three posts placed some distance away from a bucket
- see how many items of clothing can be put on!

You can add to the above activities if you wish.

7 At the end of the activities ask the children to observe how their bodies reacted to physical exercise:

- what happens to your breathing?
- what happens to your cheeks
- are you sweating?
- which parts of your body did you use most for each activity?

8 Children may like to complete **copymaster 51 (Sports)** by drawing a line from the word to the appropriate picture.

9 Ask the children to compare performances by counting the results and finding the difference. All kinds of comparisons can be made by using the numerical results of each activity, even down to finding the class 'champion'. This could then be used to explore all the issues related to winning and losing and such matters as doing better in some things and not in others.

History building block

AT1 L1, 2, 3
AT2 L1, 2, 3
AT3 L1, 2, 3

Although ancient Greece is a designated part of History Key Stage 2, this building block offers children an introduction to ancient Greece and 'opportunity to develop an awareness of the past and of ways in which it was different from the present' (Programmes of Study for Key Stage 1, History in the National Curriculum).

HISTORY ACTIVITIES

You will need a map of Europe showing Greece in relation to Britain. Also, pictures of ancient Greeks, particularly athletes.

1 Ask the children to name their favourite sports. These can be listed on a board or large sheet of paper.

2 Ask the children to draw a picture of someone taking part in their favourite sport. It might be a footballer or tennis player. Identify the particular piece of equipment used, i.e. tennis racquet, football, boxing gloves, skis, etc. Look at the special clothes worn for each sport.

3 Tell the children that many years ago (explain the term 'ancient'), long before Jesus or the prophet Mohammed were born, in a country called Greece there lived some very clever people who liked playing sports of all kinds. A big competition would be held regularly to find the best runner, thrower, jumper and fighter. Only boys and men could take part, married women were not even allowed to watch. The big competition was called the Olympic Games.

4 Look at pictures of the ancient Greeks, or listen to descriptions given. Compare the differences between the way the ancient Greeks dressed and how sportsmen and women dress today.

5 Invite the children to name (a) some sports that take place today but might not have existed then; (b) sport(s) that took place in ancient Greece and still take(s) place today.

6 Discuss what the children think about women and girls not being able to take part in sport.

7 The main sports that took place were discus throwing (there may be a need to explain or to show the children a discus), javelin throwing, running, jumping and wrestling. In groups, the children could hold their own ancient Olympics (using safe equipment such as rubber quoits instead of a discus) and find their own Olympic champions. Include girls of course and note how many are just as good as, if not better than, the boys!

RE building block

Many of the world's religions have expectations that often take the form of a promise. The nature of the promise in relation to a given undertaking is explored in this building block.

- **Note**   It is suggested that the RE unit would benefit by immediately following history.

RE ACTIVITIES

1 Discuss with the children what it is they most enjoy about playing games and taking exercise. Suggestions might include the following:

- I like playing with my friends.
- we like playing together
- I like running about
- I like kicking a ball
- we like skipping together

- it's good fun chasing each other
- I like winning.

2 Ask the children if there is anything they *don't* like about playing games. The might come up with the following:

- it's sad to lose
- I feel sad and lonely when nobody plays with me

- I hate being left out
- I don't like it when people cheat.

[3] Tell the children that when the first Olympic Games took place all those who took part had to make a promise. What do you think they promised?

[4] If boys and girls are playing together, especially in a team, what kind of promise could they make to each other? Together, shape any suggestions into their own

'Olympic Promise' that values members of the team, fair play, clapping winners, as well as those who try hard but don't necessarily win, not being selfish and observing rules. You might want to relate this to children's perceptions of the kind of behaviour that God might expect of people.

[5] Once the promise has been created, ask the children to write it out on to a certificate that could be displayed in a place for all to see.

Geography building block

Attainment Target 2: Knowledge and Understanding of Places (Geography in the National Curriculum) expects pupils to demonstrate their increasing knowledge and understanding of places in local, regional, national and international global contexts. Studying flags of different countries as seen at the Olympic Games is an excellent starting point for young children learning about the location of places.

GEOGRAPHY ACTIVITIES C52

[1] Explain to the children that our modern Olympic Games have many countries taking part. When the Games open there is a great ceremony in a place called a stadium. The athletes from each country parade around the stadium carrying the flag of their country. The procession is headed by the Olympic flag which expresses the common unity of all participants.

Together, look at some flags from other countries. Consider the colours and designs of each flag and above all, by looking at a map, discover not only which country the flag represents but also where in the world the country is.

[2] Use **copymaster 52 (Flags)** and ask the children to identify each flag shown by writing the country in the space provided. When they have done this, they can colour the flags in the correct colours.

[3] Look at a map of the British Isles. Tell the children that Britain is an island. Ask them if they know what an island is. Tell them that the British Isles are made up of four countries. Can they identify them?

[4] Ask the children to draw the flags of Scotland, Ireland and England. Explain that each has a cross – the crosses of St George (England), St Andrew (Scotland) and St Patrick (Ireland).

ASSESSMENT C53

Assessment in groups can enable individual children who may not normally contribute to a class discussion to make a contribution which can be valued by the group thus contributing towards that child's self-esteem.

[1] Spend some time talking to the children about the things that they have learned about the importance of taking regular exercise.

2 Using a fun activity (e.g. anyone wearing red, green, etc.), divide the class into five groups.

3 Give each group a question to talk about and to answer. Tell them that you will ask each group in turn what they think.

Group One	What sort of activities exercise us?
Group Two	What activities would we like to do?
Group Three	Why is exercise good for us?
Group Four	Why is food important for exercise?
Group Five	Who is able to exercise?

4 Ask each group in turn what the answer to their question is. Ask the class if there is anything else anyone wants to say.

5 Give out copies of **copymaster 53 (My personal exercise plan)** to each child and tell them that they are going to choose an activity which will give them exercise at home and that they are going to do this exercise once a day for a whole week. At the end of the week, Mum, Dad or the person who looks after them will sign it as a certificate to say that this has been completed. They will bring these back to school to keep in their personal work book.

6 Ask the children to see if they can find the flags of England, Scotland and Ireland in the Union Jack.

7 Suggest to the children that they are going to enter a sporting competition (perhaps their own Olympic Games). They will need to have their own flag which will lead the procession at the start of the games. Ask the children to design their own flag containing colours and design or pictures that mean something special to them.

HEALTHY EATING

Building blocks of the curriculum

Citizenship

- Understanding the needs, plight and priorities of others
- Taking things for granted
- Abundance and waste

RE

- 'Special' foods
- Festivals and celebrations

PE

- The human 'machine'
- Fuel for the body
- Group activities – making a machine
- Developing creativity, co-operation, confidence
- Practising balance, timing and trust

English

- Keeping a food diary

Technology

- The school kitchen
- Devising a menu
- Cooking utensils

Geography

- Interdependence
- Tracking food to the country of origin
- Labels and packaging
- Cause of famine

Environment

- Food and the environment; conditions for growth; role of humanity and the elements

Music

- Food 'sounds'
- Songs about food
- Improvising sounds and tunes using 'cooking noises'

History

- Comparing present experiences with those of the past
- Kitchens at school and at home compared to kitchens of long ago

Science

- Classification of foods
- Balanced diet
- Importance of liquid intake

Economic and industrial awareness

- Exporting and importing food

Art

- Creating a food wheel
- Making a collage/models of party food
- Decorating a diary

Mathematics

- A balanced and healthy diet – exploring data, time, proportion

INTRODUCTION

It has been estimated that up to 500 people die every day from coronary heart disease in this country; the equivalent of a Jumbo Jet crashing each day (Lynch, 1987). Coronary heart disease has been closely related to nutrition and diet and to the lifestyle that we lead. Certainly the incidence of other diseases such as some types of cancer and diabetes can be similarly related to diets low in fibre but high in saturated fats and sugar.

We are told not to consume foods containing 'E' additives and to eat foods 'low in cholesterol'. Advertising exhorts us to eat this product and to drink that. The messages are often contradictory, misleading and confusing. However, the evidence does suggest that ill-health in later life can be avoided by healthy eating during childhood, and that schools can do much to promote sensible eating behaviour through the curriculum and the social situations in which it is taken.

Curriculum Guidance 5 learning objectives

Pupils should:

- know that there is a wide variety of foods to choose from and that choice is based on needs and/or culture.
- know that food is needed for bodily health and growth and that some foods are better than others.

Teachers need to be aware of the dangers of teaching about healthy foods while selling unhealthy snacks in the tuckshop; and the need to recognise that children will come from a variety of backgrounds, cultures, races and religions where different foods will be eaten and where attitudes to food may differ from their own.

Similarly, school meals do not always provide adequate healthy food choices and cafeteria systems certainly are not conducive to social situations which may promote healthy attitudes towards eating and food.

STARTING POINTS

- Using pictures taken from magazines ask the class to identify which foods they like and dislike. As each is identified stick the pictures on to large sheets of paper.

  Remind the children that because they have different tastes some foods will appear on both lists.

- Ask the children why they like some foods and dislike others – what makes them dislike particular foods? For the foods they have selected ask if they have ever tasted them. (What is it about the foods; is it smell, taste, texture? Remember that some foods will simply be enjoyed.)

foods we like

cake
sausages
chips
bread
corn flakes
rice
eggs
curry

foods we don't like

cabbage
rice pudding
coffee
fish

- Using **copymaster 54 (Tastes)** invite the children to describe the taste of the foods given in the left-hand column by writing 'sweet', 'sour', 'salty' or 'bitter' in the right-hand column. Encourage them to add some examples of their own. This work can be related to the wordplay exercise in **Being safe** (see p. 41).

- Ask the class why they think they need food – point out that being hungry is the body's way of saying that it needs food for growing and energy. Suggest that our body is like a machine and that food is the fuel that keeps it running.

- Ask the children which foods help keep the machine 'running smoothly' and keeps them healthy. (You may wish to record these on a large sheet of paper.)

- Tell the class that they are going to find out about food and about choosing foods which will make and keep them healthy.

Science building block

> AT1 L1, 2,
> AT2 L1, 2, 3
> AT3 L1, 2

Children and adults need food for energy and growth. The simple classification of foods into different types from which children can choose is more important for healthy eating at Key Stage 1 than knowing about vitamins, portiens and carbohydrates.

SCIENCE ACTIVITIES

C55
–56

Food groups

[1] Remind children of the foods they liked/disliked. Ask them where they think those foods come from. Suggest that there are two main sources of food – animals and plants. Tell them that we normally think of plants as being either fruit or vegetables and that we sometimes turn plants into other products, e.g. wheat into flour and then into bread.

[2] Give each child a plate-sized circle of paper or card divided into three labelled sections, 'animal', 'vegetable' and 'fruit'. Using **copymaster 55 (Food groups)**, tell them to colour in the pictures of different foods, label them, cut them out and stick them on to their 'plate' to show the food groups. (If you prefer, **copymaster 60 (Food wheel)** can be used as the 'plate'.)

[3] Ask the children where they would place foods like butter, cheese, eggs, biscuits, jam.

[4] Explain to the children that we need foods from each group to give us energy, to help us grow and to keep us healthy. Discuss which we need more of and less of.

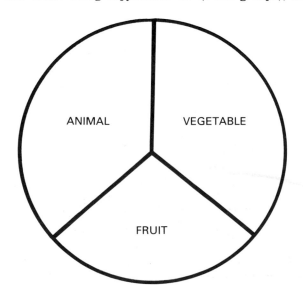

5 Ask them if they know what a vegetarian is. Draw out or explain that vegetarians choose not to eat meat for personal/religious reasons. Tell the children that this is perfectly alright as is the avoidance of any type of food for similar reasons. Tell them that what is important is having a balanced diet. That is, a diet which has elements of each food group and if one food group is left out something has to replace it.

6 Remind the class that there are foods we should eat less of because too many or too much could harm us in some way; e.g. sugar in sweets, cakes and biscuits causes tooth decay.

Drinks and drinking

1 Ask the children to bring in empty cartons, cans, pictures and containers to make a display of their favourite drinks.

2 Ask the class what their favourite drinks are.

3 Ask them why we need to drink at all. Suggest that we need liquids every day to help clean 'the inside' of our body, to keep it (the 'machine') running smoothly.

4 Ask them where the waste goes to when it comes out of our bodies – how does it come out?

5 Ask them why we drink a lot on a hot day. Suggest that sweating helps to keep us cool and stops our 'machine' from over-heating.

6 Using a lemonade bottle three-quarters filled with water, demonstrate to the children that three-quarters of our body weight is actually water and that we need to drink a lot in order to keep that proportion topped up. We can live for a very long time without food but we cannot live very long without water.

7 Discuss with the children where else we get liquids from, tell them that many of the foods we eat contain a lot of water (ask them what all plants need to survive).

A simple experiment to prove the point would be three identical plants kept in the classroom where one is watered regularly, one is watered irregularly and one is not watered at all. Tell the children to observe what happens over a period of time. (The withering plant can soon be revived provided the experiment has not gone on for too long!)

Our favourite drinks

Technology building block

AT1 L1, 2, 3
AT4 L1, 2, 3

The healthy eating context can provide pupils with the opportunity to identify and state clearly needs and opportunities for design and technological activities through investigations.

TECHNOLOGY ACTIVITIES

C56 –57

1 If your school has a functioning kitchen providing dinners have the children invite the cook(s) to come and explain how the menus for school lunches are arrived at. This could be done as a visitor exercise whereby the children:

- write to the cook(s) inviting him/her to visit their classroom to join in their work on food;
- prepare simple snacks and drinks for their visitor(s) and each other, deciding what they will have, where they will buy it from, how much money it will cost (this is a good opportunity to reinforce hygiene and

also begin to introduce a certain element of economic awareness);
- decide what questions they would like to ask of their visitor(s) and who will ask them;
- decide who will thank the visitor(s) at the end;
- discuss what they have found out;
- write letters thanking the visitor(s) for their contribution.

2 Invite individual parents to come into school to demonstrate different types of food and cooking. This is especially useful in breaking down barriers about foods/diet from differing ethnic backgrounds. Seek to invite a father along to demonstrate his culinary expertise; too often demonstrations of this kind are given by mothers.

3 In the light of the visitor(s) display/talk have the children design a 'balanced' school lunch by drawing the foods on to a piece of paper cut to make a plate or using materials, papier mâché, etc. make a 3-D meal and paint them to look like the real thing (disposable paper plates make a good base). Mount them as a collage or set out tables to look like a restaurant.

4 Using **copymasters 56 (Healthy days)** and **57 (Healthy meals)** ask the children to
- colour in the circles on copymaster 56 and cut along the dotted lines
- draw a picture of healthy food for each meal in the circles on copymaster 57
- cover each picture with the appropriate circle from copymaster 56, then ask a friend to guess what the food might be underneath.

Music building block

Food should be part of an enjoyable social activity. Music can be an expression of the enjoyment as expressed through sounds and working together.

MUSIC ACTIVITIES

1 Using classroom musical instruments (shakers, rattles, rasps, whistles) allow the children to make 'cooking noises'.

Discuss with them the sounds those noises make and how they might repeat them using their instruments:

sausages – sizzling

steam – hissing

fried eggs – crackling

crisps – crunching

kettles – whistling

rice – bubbling

popadoms – popping

2 Working in groups have the children practise and then present their cooking noises to the remainder of the class.

3 There are many songs and rhymes about food which the class can learn and sing together:
- Bananas in pyjamas
- Ten fat sausages sizzling in the pan
- Rainbow harvest
- I'm a little teapot
- Mix a pancake
- Cheese please
- The super supper march.

Geography building block

AT1 L1, 2
AT2 L1, 2, 3
AT3 L1, 2, 3
AT4 L1, 2, 3
AT5 L1, 2, 3

We obtain many food products from other countries. It is very important for children to recognise our dependence on other people in other lands and the interdependence of mankind.

GEOGRAPHY ACTIVITIES

C58

1 Ask the children to collect labels from tins and packaging or the wrapping that food comes in. (Tell them to ask their Mum, Dad or the person who looks after them first.)

2 The 'country of origin' is invariably printed on labels and packaging. Select different food products and identify their country of origin.

3 Using a large globe/world map show the children the food product and the location of the country of origin.

4 On a large world map, mark the country with a coloured flag and using a length of cotton/thread join it to the label/packaging which should be displayed alongside.

5 Use **copymaster 58 (Foods from afar?)** and ask the children to write in the space provided the country from which each meal shown originated. Afterwards, they might like to colour in the pictures.

6 Ask the class if they think everyone in the world has enough to eat. Can they think of any country where the people do not get enough to eat. (Many countries facing a famine crisis are often featured in the news.) Ask the children what name we give to this. Identify those countries on the map.

7 Ask the children what they think causes famine. Write down their ideas.

> *too many people –*
> *not enough rain –*
> *war – too wet –*
> *too hot – too cold*

8 Discuss with them how countries with plenty of food could help those countries with very little. Discuss what they could do to help.

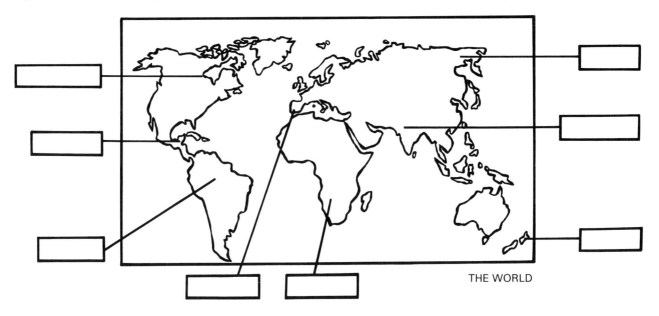

THE WORLD

PE building block

Food and exercise are very closely related. We eat food for energy which is burned up while exercising. If children do not exercise regularly then they risk becoming overweight and face the increasing risk of coronary heart disease in later life.

PE ACTIVITIES

1 Remind the children that their bodies are just like machines which need fuel to work. For them food is the fuel which is turned into energy and into all the hungry things that help them grow to be healthy adults.

2 Tell them that if machines are not worked regularly they do not work properly and break down. Suggest that our bodies also need to be exercised regularly in order to remain healthy.

3 After usual PE activities divide the class into groups of five or six and ask each class to demonstrate a 'machine' by each person taking on a working part moving in sequence and in time with the rest of the machine. This activity demonstrates creativity, co-operation, confidence and practises the skills of balance, timing and trust.

4 Ask each group, after a period of practice, to demonstrate their 'machine' to the rest of the class.

English building block

AT1 L1, 2, 3
AT2 L1, 2, 3
AT3 L1, 2, 3
AT4 L1, 2, 3
AT5 L1, 2, 3

The Curriculum Guidance 5 learning objectives state that food is needed for bodily health and growth and that there is a wide variety to choose from. For many children, what and when they eat can be an almost incidental part of their day. Before children can learn about choice and decision-making related to their diet they need to have brought to their attention their present eating habits. Explaining the use of a diary is one way this notion can be introduced and is an excellent way of enabling children to structure sequences of real events coherently and in chronological accounts'.

ENGLISH ACTIVITIES

C59 –60

1 Begin with the teacher showing the children her/his diary. Discuss the necessity of such a book; how it enables notes to be recorded, contains messages, appointments, etc. Give examples of other forms of recording or 'reminding' associated with time: the date at the top of the board, at the top of a newspaper, comic, magazine; a weather chart; the date at the top of a piece of work.

2 Ask the children to suggest all the things they do nearly every day. Under a title ('Some things we do every day') written on the board, write down the suggestions

and information given by the children. Wherever possible ask questions about the health issues involved. For example: why should we change our clothes and wash regularly? This can be linked to the next unit (**Keeping clean**).

3 Tell the children we are going to think about the food we eat during the day.

4 Using the board, write four headings: breakfast, dinner, tea/supper, snacks. Ask the children to list the favourite things they have for each meal and also what snacks they usually have.

5 Who chooses the food they eat? Who goes shopping for the family? Do they help in any way? Do they have to eat food they don't like? Does an adult tell them to eat food that is good for them even if they don't like it? Why eat at all?

6 Tell the children they are going to keep a diary of all the food they eat and drink during the day. **Copymaster 59 (My food diary)** can be sent home and parents encouraged to help.

• **Note** It is important to encourage children from all ethnic groups to state the foods they eat at home (some of which appear on school menus) and for the food to be considered in the same context as *all* food and not categorised as 'foreign food' or 'strange food'.

7 Once the information has been completed, children should allocate each food item to an appropriate section within the **Food wheel** on **copymaster 60**. They will be familiar with this exercise having carried out activity 2 in the Science building block (p. 60).

8 Ask children to compare their diary accounts of the food they eat. Perhaps they could make a list of new foods they would like to introduce into their diet which could be taken home and shown to their parents/carers.

9 Similar food diaries can be kept to record the food intake of pets or to record specified items such as fruit or sweets perhaps covering two or more days.

Mathematics building block

> AT1 L1, 2, 3
> AT5 L1, 2, 3

The idea of a balanced diet and a healthy diet requires a certain understanding of proportion and time and the ability to classify according to what things have in common with each other. These concepts and skills are as much mathematical as health related.

Gathering information and displaying it is obviously important. But using the information is essential if there is to be a meaning and purpose to the exercise of gathering.

MATHEMATICS ACTIVITIES ▶

1 Brainstorming with the class and/or using the information gathered from Science building block activity 2 and English building block activity 7, the teacher should record all the items that the children suggest fall into the categories forming each portion of the food wheel.

2 From the information collected a giant-sized food wheel for display in the classroom could be made, using cartons and wrappings brought from home to fill in the sections.

3 Without going into great detail, bring to the attention of the children foods that are high in fibre, fats, salts and sugars. Reports by the National Advisory Committee on Nutrition Education ('A Discussion paper on proposals for Nutrition Guidelines in Britain' HEC 1983, and Committee on Medical Aspects of Food Policy, Diet and Cardiovascular Disease, DHSS 1984) suggest we increase the fibre intake in our diet and lesson our intake of fats, sugars and salt.

4 Using the information from the food wheel, ask the children to devise a menu for a single meal to satisfy a visitor who insists on eating a healthy diet. A school dinner could be provided by the school cook to show how a menu is arranged and the order in which the food is served. If the school does not provide on-site cooked meals then a menu from a local restaurant will do.

The concept of time can be developed in a parallel to those of sets/proportion/classification/data gathering that have been the focus so far. Indeed, the English building block's introduction to diaries and sequencing has already begun to address the concept of time. Depending on what stage the children's knowledge and skill is at regarding time, a starting point could be the various parts of the day, i.e. dawn/early morning, mid-morning, noon/midday, mid-afternoon, early evening/dusk, night, all considered in relation to what children are doing (or eating) around those particular 'times'.

History building block

AT1 L1, 3
AT2 L1, 2, 3
AT3 L1, 2, 3

An effective way for children to learn about the past is when they are in a position to compare their own experiences with those of another age. The comparison from the past can be presented visually through pictures or experientially, by making a visit to a museum or historical place.

The focus for food and nutrition is the child's own kitchen at home or the kitchen at school. In the past, it was during medieval times that the kitchen of the castles and the manor houses really came into their own as places where magnificent feasts were prepared.

HISTORY ACTIVITIES

C61 –62

1 Begin by reciting the following nursery rhyme.

Sing a song of sixpence

Sing a song of sixpence
A pocket full of rye,
Four and twenty blackbirds
Baked in a pie.

When the pie was opened,
The birds began to sing;
Was not that a dainty dish
To set before the King?

The King was in the counting-house,
Counting out his money;
The Queen was in the parlour,
Eating bread and honey.

The maid was in the garden,
Hanging out the clothes;
When down came a blackbird
And pecked off her nose.

65

2 Tell the children that a long, long time ago the castles and big manor houses where kings and queens and lords and ladies lived had big kitchens in which many large feasts were prepared. Sometimes a large pie was prepared and inside the pastry would be placed four and twenty blackbirds. When the pie was opened out would fly the birds to everyone's surprise. Even jugglers were known to have jumped out of puddings! Children can work on **copymaster 61 (Baked in the pie)** to name the objects shown and to draw some of their own in the boxes provided.

3 Tell the children that in the kitchens of long ago the cook could only keep his/her food safe to eat for a long time by soaking it in salt or smoking it under a fire. What happens to food that is left for a long time? Place a banana on a plate and leave it in the classroom for a period of time. Record the change in the banana's condition. Other food can also be used to show decay, e.g. bread, tomatoes, cheese. A comparison can be made between food placed in the classroom exposed to the air and to food kept in a fridge.

4 Ask children to describe how their food at home is kept fresh. Refrigerators and freezers will be mentioned. Why have both? What do the stars mean on the packaging of food that is kept in a freezer?

5 In the kitchens of long ago food was cooked over an open fire. Meat, such as pigs, birds such as swans and even large fish were cooked on a spit, which is a piece of metal that went through the freshly prepared meat and placed over a fire where it was slowly turned by a kitchen boy or girl.

How is food cooked today in your kitchen? Make a drawing of what you use to cook food with in your house.

6 Discuss with the children what they think is necessary for all people who are preparing food to eat. Make up a list of rules to hang in a kitchen.

RULES FOR PREPARING FOOD

1. Inspect the food for freshness
2. Always wash your hands
3. Make sure the table-top /plate is clean
4. Wash the food
5. Make sure the food is not still frozen

7 Using **copymaster 62 (Feasts)**, ask the class to look at the feast prepared long ago. On the table below they should draw a feast that they would prepare for friends coming to a party in their house. Which feast do they think has the healthiest food? Children should be encouraged to show the kind of food they might have at home on a special occasion (see the RE building block activity 5 and *Blueprints Topics*, Knights and castles, p. 121).

RE building block

Special food is often associated with a religious festival. This is true of nearly all Faiths. This universal nature of the significance of food as part of religious celebrations is a pivotal part of any multi-faith RE syllabus where differences are acknowledged but similarities are sought.

RE ACTIVITIES

1 Working in groups, ask the children to list special foods for special occasions. Report back to the teacher who writes on the board the suggestions from each group. (There is no need to repeat any suggestion.)

> birthday cake
> samosas
> jellebies
> jelly and ice cream
> Christmas cake
> Yule log

2 Ask the children which of the special days shown on the board are holy days. Draw a coloured circle around the holy days.

3 Ask the children to name what or who is holy or special.

4 What happens during a special day? (Try to encourage and develop the idea of sharing, especially food, with others.) Ask the children to describe the foods that were eaten and *shared* during the special day(s). Pictures could be drawn or collected from books and used to illustrate a description of what took place; i.e. Christmas Dinner and its preparation at home, food at Eid, Diwali, or the Passover. Collages could be made depicting the variety of food eaten at various festivals.

5 Children can draw the foods they would have at their party using **copymaster 63 (Party time)**.

- **Note** Special days might also include days when a family was united through grief, perhaps the death of a close relative, and food such as lunch or tea was part of the occasion. Take note of this and do not dismiss it as being irrelevant.

6 Without too much difficulty it is possible to discover that nearly all major religions have feast days and particular foods associated with them. Choose a particular religious festival and list the food eaten. Ask the children to make a comparison with the food eaten at another, perhaps their own, religious festival. Ask them to write or draw the items on the list.

ASSESSMENT

Assessment can be used to check learning, correct misconceptions and to reinforce important concepts.

1 Use a fun activity to divide the class into groups of about five children. Ask them to talk together about

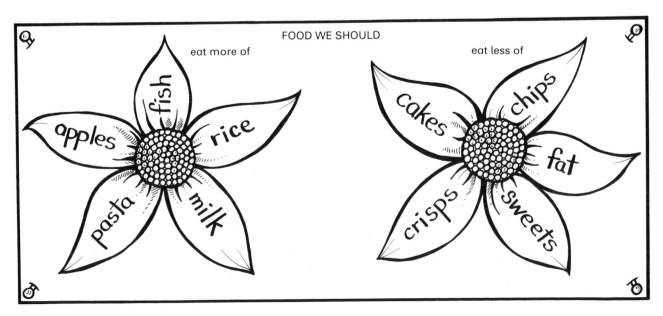

FOOD WE SHOULD

eat more of — apples, fish, rice, pasta, milk

eat less of — cakes, chips, fat, crisps, sweets

which foods they believe we should eat more of and which foods we should eat less of to remain healthy.

2 Give each group enough red petals and green petals for each group member to have one of each. (A4 sized sheets cut in petal shapes are appropriate.)

3 Tell the children to write down on a green petal, the name of a food we should eat more of, and on a red petal the name of a food we should eat less of.

4 When every child has done this give each group a large piece of paper on which a yellow circle (flower centre) has been previously glued.

5 Tell the groups to assemble a red flower and a green flower by sticking the appropriate petals around the flower centre.

6 Display the finished 'flowers' and summarise for the children the different foods they have placed in each category. Check misplaced foods/inappropriate foods, using the activity to reinforce the healthy diet message.

KEEPING CLEAN

Building blocks of the curriculum

Citizenship

- Being responsible for oneself – looking after oneself
- Who cares for me?

History

- Personal hygiene in the past – differences between rich and poor

Mathematics

- Applying and handing data
- Counting and simple graphwork

Environment

- Clean/dirty environments

Geography

- The weather and appropriate clothing
- Weather charts

English

- Poetry as a means of creating images and describing emotions; speaking and listening

Music

- Songs and rhymes relating to body awareness and to keeping clean
- Creating sounds

RE

- Stories from different faiths/religions
- The importance of water in religious rites

PE

- Washing after exercise

Art

- Primary colours and secondary colours

Science

- Germs, microbes and magnifying
- Transmission of illness and disease

INTRODUCTION

Young children need increasing opportunities to take responsibility for aspects of their own health and to make decisions and choices about certain activities. Keeping clean is an important aspect of health where they can take responsibility for themselves effectively and where teachers can encourage and support healthy routines developed at home. Being responsible for one's own cleanliness, teeth cleaning and, for younger children, dressing appropriately, not only develops sensible and appropriate personal behaviour but fosters a sense of achievement, self-confidence and self-esteem.

Curriculum Guidance 5 learning objectives

Pupils should:

- understand the need for and be able to practise simple personal routines, e.g. washing hands, cleaning teeth, using a handkerchief.
- begin to understand that some diseases are infectious and that transmission may be reduced when simple safe routines are used.

STARTING POINTS

- Ask the children what they do to look after themselves at home; record their ideas on a large sheet of paper.

> things we cannot
>   do for ourselves
> · cook food
> · wash own clothes
> · walk to school
> · stay up late
> · take medicines

Similarly ask them what they do to look after themselves at school.

> Don't sneeze over people or food
>   ~ do use a hanky
> Don't handle food with dirty hands
>   ~ do wash your hands
> Don't let flies land on food
>   ~ cover food up

- Discuss with the children if they have always been able to do those things. Consider the importance of Mums and Dads, or whoever looks after us, when we are babies and small.

- Ask if there are any things they cannot do for themselves or are not allowed to do. Are there things that their older brothers and sisters can do but they are not allowed to do, or are there things they are allowed to do but younger brothers and sisters are not?

> things we can do at home
> wash ourselves
> get dressed   go to bed
> brush our teeth
> brush our hair

- Tell the children that they are going to find out about keeping clean and why being able to look after oneself is very important.

- **Note** Make sure that your school toilets have hot water, soap and clean towels if health promoting messages are not to be contradicted for children. (Some aspects of this topic relate to **Being safe**.)

70

Science building block

AT1 L1, 2, 3
AT2 L1, 2, 3

The concept of 'germs' is most important if children are going to understand the need for washing hands before handling food, and other basics of personal hygiene. A scientific perspective involves introducing children to ideas about keeping healthy and 'maintaining their welfare by knowing about their needs and understanding the care required'.

SCIENCE ACTIVITIES

C64 –65

1 Find out from the children what they think causes things like colds, flu and sickness. Develop the idea that there are tiny organisms which are commonly called 'germs' but are so small we can only see them with a microscope which can magnify them. Tell them that these germs should really be called microbes. Tell them not all germs or microbes make us ill. Indeed, most are harmless, and some are beneficial or vital to human life.

2 Ask the children for names of some common illnesses caused by germs.

3 Place the children in small groups, each having a magnifying glass (hand held or on a tripod). Give each group some everyday items like feathers, dead insects, leaves, etc.

4 Ask them to look at their items and on a clean sheet of paper, draw what they see. (Remind them that they won't actually *see* any germs, but suggest that what they are seeing is larger because it is viewed through a magnifying glass.)

5 Discuss with the children what they saw. (Use their drawings for developing paintings or collage work or simply display their drawings.)

6 Ask them to look at their own hands through the magnifiers – are their hands dirty or clean?

7 With the class, discuss how they think germs or microbes are spread. Write down their ideas. You may need to offer ideas too.

8 Discuss with the children the best way of preventing the spread of microbes or germs (see *Blueprints Topics*, Pets, p. 24).

> how germs are spread
> sneezing   coughing
> flies   handling pets
> touching food with
> dirty hands

9 In groups of two or three, the children can play the **Beat the germs** game using **copymaster 64** as the board. A die is thrown by each player in turn. The first home wins – or do they? What lessons are learned?

10 Make a class list of do's and don'ts for keeping germs under control.

> things we can do at school
> change for P.E.
> wash hands before dinner
> choose lunch
> go out to play

11 As a class, practise hand-washing in the toilets and provide plenty of opportunities, especially before lunch, for children to wash their hands.

12 Consolidate work on the spread of germs by asking children to complete **copymaster 65 (Spreading germs)**. The pictures can be matched by drawing connecting lines between them.

Mathematics building block

> AT1 L1, 2, 3
> AT2 L1
> AT5 L1, 2, 3

There is much evidence to suggest that thorough tooth cleaning not only helps prevent tooth decay but, more importantly, gum disease which can be serious in later life.

By using and applying mathematics, particularly in number and handling data, children can learn about the arrangement of teeth and about the care necessary to maintain their health.

MATHEMATICS ACTIVITIES

C66 –67

Examining teeth

1 Arrange the class in small groups and give each group a non-breakable mirror.

2 Ask the children to smile at each other – what can they see? Have they always had teeth? Discuss why babies don't (as a rule) have teeth when they are born (i.e. the need to suckle milk from mother's breast, cannot eat solid food).

3 Who has already lost some teeth? In pairs and using mirrors, children can 'inspect' their own teeth and those of their partners. Why have some lost some of their teeth?

4 Ask what their teeth are for. Write down their suggestions.

5 Tell the children that the first teeth they have are called 'milk teeth' and that these will drop out by themselves to make space for their stronger permanent second teeth when they are about six or seven. Tell them that when they are grown up they will have thirty-two teeth, provided they are properly taken care of!

6 Using the mirrors, ask the children to count up how many teeth they now have. Ask each child in turn and record these numbers for the whole class.

7 Discuss with the children how they think they could show these numbers of teeth. Suggest that using a class list they could draw and count out a tooth for each number to show each person and then add them up for the whole class sticking them on to a large sheet.

making faces

Ali ....20 teeth
Andrew ....22 teeth
Carmen ....21 teeth

Brushwork

1 Having previously asked the children to bring in their toothbrushes (or having provided each child with

72

a new tooth brush – a number of toothpaste and toothbrush manufacturers will provide teeth care packs for your school through their oral hygiene service, free of charge) ask the children to brush their teeth as they do at home.

2 With the children working in pairs, have each child brush their teeth while the other child, using a stop watch or clock, time how long they take to brush their teeth.

3 Identify the children who were the quickest and slowest brushers. With the children, consider which length of time they think is the best time for getting teeth clean.

4 Give each child a disclosing tablet (available from the chemist). When it is their turn, have each child chew a tablet thus staining the plaque on the teeth a bright pink. Now tell them to brush their teeth again, taking care to remove all of the pink-stained plaque; the partner should again time the length of brushing. How long did it take? (Consider the guesses made earlier when discussing the length of time needed to brush teeth properly. Were the children faster or slower this time and did it take longer to remove all of the pink stain which showed the 'dirty' teeth?)

5 Use this as an opportunity to demonstrate the correct way of brushing teeth and gums to keep healthy.

6 Record the fastest and slowest times before the disclosure tablets and compare them with the post-disclosure brushing times. Reinforce the need for children not only to brush their teeth and gums carefully but to spend longer doing it than they normally think is sufficient. An egg-timer (three to four minutes) in the bathroom may help.

7 Children can fill in **copymaster 66 (Brushing our teeth)** to summarise what they have learned about cleaning their teeth.

Tooth decay

1 Ask the children what things are bad for their teeth. Write these things down.

sugar
sweets
cakes
ice cream
cola
toffees

2 Why are these things bad for your teeth? (i.e. because sugar is a key factor in causing tooth decay).

3 Consider with the children what foods they think are 'good' for their teeth. Again write these down.

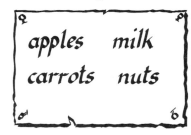

apples   milk
carrots   nuts

drinks bad for our teeth

foods bad for our teeth

foods good for our teeth

4 Using magazine pictures or those drawn by the children develop a display to show sets of food good for our teeth and sets of food bad for our teeth.

5 Remind children that they should brush their teeth after meals and that although fruit and raw carrots are 'good' for teeth and gums they do not clean teeth and are not a substitute for brushing.

6 Ask them to decide which foods shown on **copymaster 67 (Sweet tooth)** are bad for our teeth by encircling them and drawing a connecting line to the dustbin.

If your school provides snacks at lunchtime and at break for the children, are there sugar-free alternatives and savouries or fruit available for them to choose – can you restrict rather than ban the sales of sweets? Also, avoid giving sweets as a reward for good work, otherwise you will be giving conflicting messages!

Geography building block

> AT1 L1, 2
> AT3 L2, 3

'Pupils should observe and describe weather conditions and changes' and 'investigate the effects weather has on them and their surroundings' (Programme of Study for Key Stage 1). Wearing appropriate clothing and changing clothing in order to keep clean is an important part of personal hygiene. The weather usually dictates what we wear and so choosing and changing clothing is an important part of being responsible for ourselves.

GEOGRAPHY ACTIVITIES

C68 –69

1 If you haven't already got one in your class, make a simple weather chart to show the days months and type of weather.

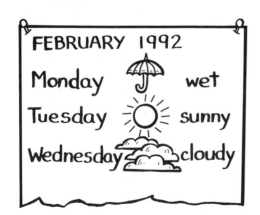

2 Each day discuss the weather and make different pupils in the class responsible for recording the weather. A beaker could also be used for collecting rainwater and some children could measure the amount of rainfall. Different units of measurement can be used such as widths of fingers, unifix and pencil widths.

3 Discuss with the children what clothes they should wear on each occasion and why those clothes are necessary.

4 The children can use **copymaster 68 (Clothes for all weathers)** and fill in the correct words next to the pictures.

5 Have a 'dressing up box' of items so the children can select different clothes appropriate to the weather, including suitable footwear.

6 Divide the class into groups and have each group responsible for making a 'life-sized child' collage to show a particular type of weather and the appropriate clothing.

Display in the classroom/school.

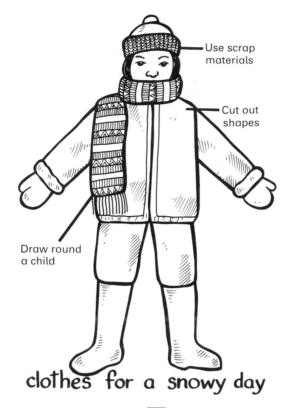

Use scrap materials

Cut out shapes

Draw round a child

clothes for a snowy day

7 With the class, draw up two lists: (a) What things make our clothes dirty? (b) Why should we change our clothes?

Display in the classroom.

8 Give each child a copy of **copymaster 69 (Packing for holiday)** and ask them to draw a circle around the items they would need for keeping clean on holiday. 'Pack' these items by drawing a connecting line into the suitcase.

Art building block

Using primary colours (red, yellow and blue) and secondary colours of green, purple and orange – black and white are not part of the colour spectrum but could be used in the context of making that particular point – consider feet in the context of personal hygiene.

ART ACTIVITIES

1 Provide the children with large enough pieces of paper for them to trace carefully round the outside of their shoes.

2 When they have done this have them place their bare feet on the shoe outline and tell them to draw round their foot.

3 Tell them to paint the part that is their foot in a bright colour. Use only a primary colour. What a primary and secondary colour is should be discussed beforehand. Particularly, show the primary colour and its complementary secondary colour – red/green, blue/orange, yellow/purple. Then have the children paint the shoe outline in a secondary colour that is complementary to the colour chosen to paint the foot outline.

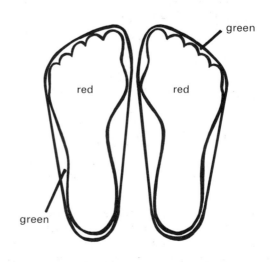

green

red   red

green

75

4 Discuss with the children how well their feet fit inside their shoes and how important wearing properly fitting shoes is for the development of feet. (Ask the school nurse to put you in touch with a chiropodist who would be willing to come in and talk to children about the care of their feet. It would be a good idea to invite parents to the talk.)

5 Using scissors, instruct the children to cut out the shoe and foot outlines. Place the foot outline on that of the shoe and then create a 'trail' around the classroom, up the walls and across the ceiling as though someone had walked there.

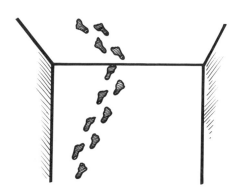

6 Remind children how important it is to wash feet regularly, to dry the area in between the toes properly and to change socks.

Music building block

There are plenty of rhymes and songs which relate to body awareness which can be cross-referenced with **Keeping clean**:

- This is the way we wash our hands
- Doctor Foster went to Gloucester
- Allouette – Oh, I wash my lovely legs
- Head, shoulders, knees and toes.

MUSIC ACTIVITIES

1 Invent a 'musical' based on keeping clean, e.g. King Bacteria versus Queen Clean and her minister, Archduke Antiseptic.

2 Record on tape washing noises: hands, hair, teeth, clothes, etc. Use them as introductions or as backing to some of the songs suggested above.

RE building block

Water and cleansing feature in varying degrees of significance in a number of the world's religions. The Christian faith has washing and cleansing associated with symbolic acts of purification of the soul and washing away of original sin.

RE can introduce this concept, particularly emphasising baptism, making the link between washing being synonymous with important aspects of personal hygiene.

RE ACTIVITIES

This preliminary work can also be used for introducing the work undertaken in the History building block for this unit.

1 Ask the children to list all the things in their

house, other than themselves, that need regular washing (i.e. dishes, floors, clothes, sinks, baths, toilets, cars, etc.).

Note that this could be an opportunity to expand the

Things that need regular washing

dishes
clothes
baths
floors
sinks

discussion on gender in relation to who does what work regarding the upkeep of the house (see **Families**, English building block activity 5, p. 32).

2 How do these objects become dirty?

3 Using **copymaster 70 (Being dirty – getting clean)**, ask the children to match the sources of dirt shown on the left-hand side with the pictures on the right-hand side. This can be done by drawing connecting lines or by cutting out the pictures and rearranging them.

4 Now ask the following questions:

- why should a dirty floor be washed?
- why should dirty dishes be washed?
- why should a dirty car be cleaned?
- why should a dirty sink be cleaned?
- why should dirty clothes be washed?
- why should dirty hands be washed?
- why should a dirty body be washed?

Make the point that water is an essential part of the cleaning process.

5 Ask the children if anyone belongs to a particular religion – Christianity, Hinduism, Sikhism, Judaism, Islam, etc. – and to invite them to tell the other children anything they know about their religion.

6 Discuss with the children the experiences of those who have been christened or baptised. Make the point that it is a way that Christians become members of the church. Concentrate the discussion around the following questions:

- where does the christening take place?
- what colour does the baby usually wear?
- who usually attends the ceremony?
- who are godparents?
- what promises do the godparents make?
- what does the priest do?
- why does the priest pour water over the head of the baby?

7 Tell the children the story of Adam and Eve.

8 Explain to the children that Christians believe that unhappiness and evil came into the world because Adam and Eve disobeyed God. By listening to Jesus people can become good again and that by washing the child's head at the time of christening, Christians see the water as washing away the old wrongs that Adam and Eve did, giving the person a new start as a person who follows the teachings of Christ. Emphasise the connection between water and cleansing.

Although some research may be required, this work could be extended by referring to Hinduism's symbolic cleaning out of the bad Karma in the ninth and final ceremony for birth, by completely cutting off the hair of the child. Also, how in Sikhism, following the birth of the child, the infant is washed and the words of the Mool Mantra – the first verses of the Holy Scriptures, the Guru Granth Sahib – are whispered into the baby's ear. Similarly, in Islam, following the birth and washing of the baby, the father or Imam (teacher) will immediately whisper the words from the Iquhamat. In multi-racial schools the children and their parents will willingly provide the information required based on their own experiences.

History building block

AT1 L1, 2, 3
AT2 L1, 2, 3

A common cause of illness in the past was the overwhelming filfth and unhygienic conditions experienced by people in their daily lives and particularly those experienced by people living in the towns and cities. But it was not merely lack of sanitation, rubbish thrown into streets and streams and general health hazards. Attention to personal hygiene was minimal even for the wealthy and nobility.

HISTORY ACTIVITIES

The preliminary work suggested in the building block for RE can also be applied here, either initially or as a revision exercise.

1 Ask the children to describe all the things necessary to keep clean and smelling fresh. Be sensitive towards any child that might through no fault of their own have problems with personal hygiene.

2 Tell the children about the first Queen Elizabeth of England who lived a long time ago. Show pictures of her and give some background information about the way people generally lived and some of the events that took place, i.e. the Spanish Armada, etc.

3 Using pictures from different sources, compare the differences between the Queen and a poor person of her realm.

4 In groups, ask the children to describe how they imagine the bathrooms of the Queen and the poor

person. Suggest they draw what they think each bathroom might look like.

5 Point out to the children that there were no bathrooms in either the castles or grand houses in which the rich people lived nor in the homes of poor people. Discuss the consequences of not having a bathroom.

6 Tell the children that Queen Elizabeth I was known to have had very bad breath and poor teeth. She seldom bathed, perhaps only once a year, or washed her hair. As a group or individual activity, ask the children to write a letter to the Queen telling her what she would do to keep clean and what things are likely to happen to her if she changes her ways.

7 Ask the children to cut out the princesses from **copymaster 71 (Cleanliness castle)** and use them as counters with dice to play the game. The princesses see a prince arriving at the castle door. They each race to the bathroom hoping to be the first there. Who wins?

English building block

AT1 L1, 2, 3
AT2 L1, 2, 3
AT3 L1, 2, 3

Poetry is an important medium for developing skills for listening, speaking, reading and writing. For one thing, children actually enjoy poetry; and a poem is a compact entity containing a number of ideas and images, and capable of arousing a whole range of emotions. It is because of this that poetry is a powerful and enjoyable way for children to learn important messages concerning their health.

ENGLISH ACTIVITIES

C72 –73

1 Distribute **copymaster 72 (Olivia takes the plunge – poem)** and read the poem to the class.

Olivia takes the plunge

Olivia stood before the sink
About to take the plunge
She took the soap into her hands
And rubbed away the gunge.

She wiped her face, her knees and legs
And gently washed her bottom
But Mum got cross for her knicks were on
Which clearly she'd forgotten!

She washed her neck and then her feet
And in between her toes
She even washed behind her ears
And the inside of her nose.

She washed her tummy and down her back
She scrubbed her perky chin
She washed away her puppy fat
Until she seemed quite thin.

So finally, when all was done
She brushed her teeth and finished
And when she pulled the plug away
She found that she had vanished!

2 Using **copymaster 73 (Olivia takes the plunge – drawing)**, invite the children to name and label parts of the body Olivia washed. Which did she wash first? Which parts of the body did Olivia leave out?

3 Ask the children to identify the rhyming words of the poem.

4 Suggest that some children might like to learn the poem, which could then be recited while other children perform washing actions to the words.

5 Select various health-related themes and give children the opportunity to make up rhyming couplets of their own.

6 Ask the children to make up a comic strip set of drawings showing Olivia during each stage of washing herself. Prompts could come from each sentence of the poem. Display these around the classroom as important and useful reminders for keeping clean.

ASSESSMENT

Reassuring parents that the school is supporting them and not challenging or confronting aspects of health behaviour is essential.

1 Remind children of all the things that they said they could do to look after themselves at home and at school.

2 On a previously prepared class chart have the children record when they have washed their hands before lunch, after going to the toilet, remembered to bring a hanky, etc., by sticking on a self-adhesive star or smiling face. (Remind them that this is not a competition but simply a way for them to record their own 'performance'.)

3 Involve parents by sending home **copymaster 74 (Involving parents)** for the children's parents or guardian(s) to fill in.

	hanky	toilet	dinner
Ali	✳ ✳ ✳ ✳	✳ ✳ ✳ ✳ ✳ ✳	✳ ✳ ✳ ✳
Shenaz	✳ ✳	✳ ✳ ✳	✳ ✳ ✳ ✳
Caroline	✳	✳ ✳ ✳ ✳	✳ ✳ ✳
Donna	✳ ✳ ✳	✳ ✳ ✳ ✳ ✳	✳ ✳ ✳ ✳ ✳
Dean	✳ ✳	✳ ✳ ✳	✳ ✳ ✳

THE ENVIRONMENT

Building blocks of the curriculum

Citizenship

- The importance of the environment regarding a person's quality of life
- Effect of pollution and the failure to maintain the environment
- Duty towards the environment

Music

- Making musical instruments from discarded materials

History

- Potential for comparing rural/urban environments past and present
- Differences between past and present times; the development of clean drinking water

Mathematics

- Collecting data
- Making conclusions

Geography

- Different environments – natural and man-made

Environment

- The effect of the environment on a person's health
- Role of mankind in maintaining and understanding his/her environment

Art

- Market research
- Making a litter monster
- Decorating a tidy box
- Creating a litter collage
- Painting portraits

RE

- Rules: highway code, country code, stranger danger, school rules, green cross code
- The Bible, the Qu'ran, the Talmud

Science

- Planning, hypothesising, predicting, investigating
- Exploring and examining the environment
- Seeking and interpreting evidence

PE

- Where in the environment physical exercise can take place (see **Families**)

English

- Independent writing
- Television and newspaper reports
- Issues concerned with pollution
- Feelings

Economic and industrial awareness

- Disposable packaging and the cost to the environment

Technology

- See music

INTRODUCTION

'Faced with air pollution, global warming, the destruction of the rain forests, the advance of the deserts, the almost daily extinction of species, we have belatedly become aware of how fragile our planet is. Decisions about the environment affect the quality of life both now and in the future' (NCC, 1990).

It is important to recognise that the quality of life, and especially our health, is affected by environmental factors. Where we live, social, physical and economic factors will all have an impact on our well being.

Whether these are apparent through pollution and the failure to maintain natural areas, or simply through keeping the school or locality free from litter is not an issue. However, it is important for children to recognise and be aware of the link that exists between the environment and health issues; and in so doing, become increasingly able, not only to respect and care for their environment but also to avoid those places which may be potentially dangerous or harmful to them.

Curriculum Guidance 5 learning objectives

Pupils should:

- know that there is a range of environments, e.g. home, school, work, natural, built, urban, rural.
- know that individuals are part of their environments and have some responsibility for their care; develop an understanding of how and why rules are made concerning the school and other environments.
- know about some common illnesses and understand simple preventive health tasks that they should undertake each day.

STARTING POINTS

C75 –76

- Ask the children what they think an 'environment' is. Write down their ideas on a large sheet of paper or board.

where we live

the park

the garden the ocean

the shops the countryside

where animals live

- Develop the idea that there are different types of 'environments' and that some are natural and some are man-made.

- Show them pictures of hot environments, cold environments, urban environments and so on. Ask them which are natural and which are man-made.

- Using **copymasters 75** and **76 (Man-made or natural?, 1 and 2)**, tell the children to cut out each picture and place it in the space which shows if it is a man-made or a natural environment.

- Ask the children which environment they know best and in which they feel safe, happy and healthy. (This can be related to work on **Being safe**.) Write down or discuss their suggestions.

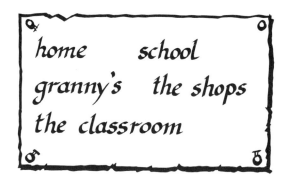

home   school

granny's   the shops

the classroom

- Ask the children who helps to look after their environment and helps to keep it clean, safe and healthy.

- Ask them what would happen if the environment in which they live wasn't kept clean. Develop the idea that a 'dirty' environment isn't a healthy one. Ask them what word we use for things that spoil the environment. Invite them to give some examples of 'pollution' that they know of (see *Blueprints Topics*, Water, p. 7).

the binmen
mummy and daddy
a police officer
road sweepers

- Tell the children that they are going to look at ways of helping to keep their environment safe and healthy.

English building block

AT1 L1, 2, 3
AT2 L1, 2, 3
AT3 L1, 2, 3
AT4 L1, 2, 3
AT5 L1, 2, 3

It is very important that children have opportunities to produce independent pieces of writing. To be able to work with others, to show work to others and to say what it is about are important factors in raising self-esteem and self-confidence.

ENGLISH ACTIVITIES

1 Tell the children to watch the television to find out about a current pollution/environmental problem. (You may wish to bring in some newspaper headlines to discuss as well.)

2 Invite the class in their 'table groups' to tell each other in turn what the pollution was, how it was caused, and what was being done to improve things.

3 Discuss with the children that television, radio and newspapers are very important because they 'tell the world' when there is a problem. Tell them that as a class they are going to make a newspaper which will tell the school about some 'pollution' in their environment.

4 Consider with the children things which might loosely be called pollution in and around the school and in their homes. Ask each child to write a short piece about that pollution and to say how they feel about it. Are they happy, sad, angry, worried, about it?

5 When they are satisfied with their 'article' have them transfer it on to the computer. You may have given them the opportunity to create their story directly on to the computer. Print their stories and ask them each to draw and colour a picture to illustrate it. Then ask them to read their stories to each other.

6 Cut out their stories and pictures and mount them on large sheets of paper in the style of a tabloid newspaper. This can be displayed in the classroom or in a space that other children use on a regular basis.

THE WESTMOUNT SCHOOL TIMES by Class 1

LITTER by Richard

WHAT WE EAT by Sundeep

Holiday Time by Razia

SMOKE by Ann

Competition

ON SALE HERE!

RE building block

Children's lives are governed by rules imposed by caring adults. It is important that they should know what rules are and why they exist.

RE ACTIVITIES

C77 –78

1 Invite the children to say what rules they should obey to keep safe and healthy. (This can be linked to activity 4 in the assessment section of **Being safe** (p. 47) as well as other areas of the unit.) Ask them why we need rules and what might happen if some people do not follow or obey those rules? Suggest that if we do not act in a caring (responsible) way then someone might get hurt as a result.

2 Play a round of 'What if?' by asking the class to respond to the following questions. (You may well wish to add some of your own or alternatively ask the children to create some of their own.)

- What if I left a broken bottle on the beach?
- What if I leave the gate to the field open?
- What if I throw my empty crisp packet on the path?
- What if I do not cross the road at the crossing?
- What if I do not wash my hands before I eat?
- What if I talk to a stranger?
- What if I throw rubbish in the canal/river/pond?
- What if I leave medicine lying around?
- What if I smoke a cigarette?
- What if I play with matches?

Discuss the implications of each statement with them. **Copymasters 77** and **78 (What if …?, 1 and 2)** can be used to highlight the consequences of these actions.

3 Discuss with the class where they can find rules that are commonly used by people to live by. Write their suggestions down.

> the Bible
> the green
>   cross code
> school rules
> the Qu'ran
> the Talmud

> the highway code
> the country code
> stranger danger
> football rules
> the law
> netball rules

4 In groups, tell the children to think of some simple rules that would help keep the school as a healthy place in which to live (i.e. a healthy environment). Provide each group with a large sheet of paper on which to write and illustrate their rules.

5 Invite the children to say what they can do to help care for their environment. Together, consider whether they (including the teacher!) keep these rules at home as well.

- **Note** It is important that these concepts and skills are seen to be transferable between different environments.

Science building block

| AT1 L1, 2, 3 |
| AT2 L1, 2, 3 |
| AT3 L1, 3 |

This building block concentrates on AT1, Scientific Investigation: planning, hypothesising, predicting, carrying out investigations, interpreting results and findings, above all, concentrating on what counts as evidence are all part of Science and the environment.

SCIENCE ACTIVITIES

C79 –80

1 Ask the children to name all the places in and around the school that are likely to be used by children and grown-ups. Record all the places on a large sheet of paper or board.

> *places in the school used by people :*
> *corridors classroom staffroom playground hall office toilets*

2 Tell the children that in groups they are going to go to some of the places they have named and bring back proof that people do go there. Explain that some proof might be too difficult to bring. Discuss other ways of recording proof. Tell them that the word 'evidence' is another word for proof.

Ensure that the places young children are sent to are safe environments. It might be a good idea to appoint a group leader, perhaps a child whose confidence needs a boost or one who needs to prove that they can act in a responsible way. Talk about the meaning of trust.

3 When they have returned, examine the evidence and ask each child to record the type of evidence brought back on **copymaster 79 (Investigating)**.

4 Discuss with the children the fact that sometimes people are careless and neglectful towards the places they use. What might his mean and how might this apply to the places they have just visited?

5 Repeat the visit exercise but this time ask the children to bring or report back on the evidence of neglect (if there isn't any, then full marks! Use that as an example of people taking care of the place).

6 Using this evidence discuss who in the school is responsible for its upkeep. The discussion might focus on:

- who runs the school?
- who is responsible for any mess or damage?

- if a person sees any mess or damage who do they tell?
- who can put things right?
- how do you tell people that they are careless or neglectful, especially if they are older and bigger than you?
- what if people are caring and look after the place they have been in, are they praised?

7 Record a taped message of what you have seen (the evidence), both good and bad things. Mention the things you have talked about. Send the tape to each class and ask the teacher to play it to the children. Say you would like to hear what the children feel about the things you have said and would therefore like a reply.

8 Some people don't take care of where they live, work, play or pass through. They make things around us quite unpleasant. Using **copymaster 80 (Pollution)** ask the children to draw a line from each form of pollution represented to the box in which it belongs. Four different colours can be used.

> *proof of people using places in school :*
>
> *place   proof*
> *corridors   ~children's work*
> *classroom ~chalk*
> *staffroom ~tea cup*
> *playground~ litter*

Mathematics building block

AT1 L1, 2, 3
AT2 L1, 2
AT4 L1, 2, 3
AT5 L1, 2, 3

Gathering and storing data, weighing and recording are the activities central to Mathematics and the environment within this building block. Collecting and presenting data in various forms is a common Mathematics activity for young children. What this building block seeks to do is to encourage children to interpret data and take consequential action.

MATHEMATICS ACTIVITIES

1. Ask the children whereabouts in the school is litter most likely to be found.

2. Identify where in the school are the litter bins stationed. This could be pinpointed on a basic map of the school premises. Then form groups and making sure that the school caretaker is informed beforehand so that she/he doesn't empty the bins, each group should choose a litter bin and each day should empty the litter collected from the bin into a bin liner provided by the teacher. One group should collect litter that has not been placed in a bin but has been discarded around the school premises.

3. At a particular time, perhaps at the end of afternoon play when all the litter has been collected, each group should (a) weigh the litter; (b) sort the litter into groups, e.g. crisp packets, sweet wrappers, biscuit wrappers, other, etc.

4. Each group should keep a daily diary noting the results and any other comments relating to what they saw in and around the collecting area, particularly regarding the use of the litter bin. It is possible for this activity to occur throughout a week or just for a day. if it is a day activity then the litter could be collected from the bins on three occasions, perhaps at the end of each playtime.

5. Ask each group to report back to the class on what they have seen, the amount collected and where they collected the litter from. Together, consider the following:

(a) on which day was the most litter collected?
(b) where was the most litter collected from?
(c) how does litter in the classroom compare with the litter collected in the playground? Is there more litter in the classroom bin than in the playground bin? Is it a different kind of litter? Why might that be?
(d) which group of litter, i.e. crisps, sweets, etc., had the most either by weight or number?

6. Now ask how much all the litter collected during the day/week weighs. How much does all the litter not placed in litter bins weigh?

7. Ask the children what lessons have been learned from their survey. How is it that some litter was found outside the litter bins?

8. How can the school ensure that as many people as possible use the litter bins provided?

Art building block

There is a range of art activities for young children to undertake in relation to the environment, but following on from the Mathematics building block it is suggested that children consider how to make the school litter bins more attractive. This will involve researching people's colour preference and what kind of things might make them stop and look.

ART ACTIVITIES

1 Following on from the discussion held earlier regarding the use of litter bins and how to ensure that people use them, say to the children that they are going to have to make the bins really stand out so that people take notice of them when they pass them by and will always remember where they are.

2 Ask the children each to think of something to do that sets out to attract somebody's attention. They might: wear funny clothes, say strange things, move in a strange way, they might sing and/or dance, pull a funny face or pretend to be someone or something quite different from themselves.

Point out to the children that they are being quite different from their usual selves and perhaps this is a good starting point – how do we make the litter bins stand out and look quite different from their usual appearance.

3 Have a look at the shape and size of a litter bin. Consider what changes could be made in terms of what area could be covered and where additions could be made. Who will use the bin? What ideas might they have?

4 In groups organise some 'market research' (this would be a good opportunity to discuss with the children that the people who make television advertisements and advertisements in comics, magazines and papers often have the same jobs as they are setting out on when trying to make the advertisement attractive and stand out from all the others). Some groups should target a class, others the staff, the cooks, visitors and parents.

5 Find out (why not use the term 'research'?) which are peoples' favourite colours and list these on a large sheet of paper.

6 If they were to buy a picture for their room or house, what kind of scene would they choose? The children can use **copymaster 81 (Favourite picture)** to help them with their survey.

7 Each group should consider the evidence they have collected and set about deciding how they will make their litter bin more attractive to those who use them.

8 Each child in the group should make a drawing using colours, and this should then be pooled and discussed by the others in the group to decide which design/drawing they will choose (of course, it might be a combination of ideas). They will also need to decide which materials to use and who does what.

9 The finished results might then be presented with a problem, if it hasn't already been thought of, e.g. how do we make the bin waterproof? To avoid disappointment it could be said that artists and designers often create their ideas using material that they know and like. A manufacturer would make the idea in the materials most suitable.

10 Are the children 'manufacturers' or 'designers'?

Other ideas for art and the environment
- Make a litter monster.
- Decorate your own tidy box.
- Create a litter collage.
- Draw/Paint a portrait of a person who spoils the environment.

Make a litter monster

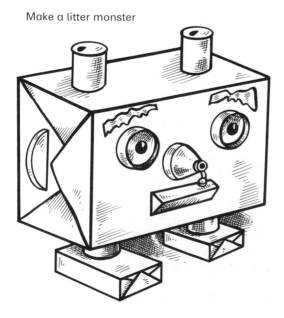

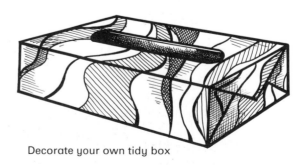

Decorate your own tidy box

Geography building block

AT1 L1, 2, 3
AT2 L1, 2, 3
AT3 L1, 2, 3
AT4 L1, 2
AT5 L1, 2, 3

This building block seeks to address a range of geographical skills, such as identifying land and sea on maps, the use of symbols for depicting physical features, and aspects of environmental geography focusing on how extraction of natural resources affects the environment, and to consider ways in which they can improve their own environment.

GEOGRAPHY ACTIVITIES

C82 –84

1 Ask the children to state where trees grow. Write their suggestions on the board or a large sheet of paper.

> where trees grow
>
> in gardens   in parks
>
> in forests   in fields
>
> on hills and mountains
>
> by roadsides

2 Ask them to state what trees give us. Write their suggestions on a board or a large sheet of paper.

Explain that trees give us wood and, using **copymaster 82 (Made from wood)**, tell the children to write down the names of as many wooden objects they can think of.

3 Discuss with the class that some countries in the world have lots of trees and some have very few trees.

4 Give each child a copy of **copymaster 83 (World map)** and, using the simple tree outline as a symbol, show the children where on the world map there are countries with many trees, i.e. Brazil, Canada, Norway, Sweden, etc. Ask the children to draw the tree symbol in the places you have shown.

5 Discuss what a symbol is. Where else in our environment do we see symbols? Consider how useful a symbol is on a map; note especially that it can be read by people of any language who would be likely to know instantly what is meant.

6 Ask the children to think of other symbols for their map. What would they use for:

- an ocean?
- a river?
- a mountain?
- a town?
- a hill?
- a road?
- a desert?

7 Suggest they put some of these on their map. They can make the locations up but they must have the right symbol for the sea. Alternatively, the children may want to make up their own map and place symbols appropriately on them. Use **copymaster 84 (Island map)** and ask the children to invent their own island showing all the main geographical features on it.

8 Tell the children there are many forests in the world, some of which are being cut down very quickly. Some trees are cut down because their wood is needed. Cutting some trees down is alright but if many trees are cut down too quickly then there can be problems. What sort of problems do they think there could be?

9 Because our trees are important to us we need to make sure they keep healthy. What do trees need to keep healthy? Suggestions should include: water, air, good soil, sunlight.

10 What do people need in order to stay healthy? (Remind the class of work they have done for **Exercising** and **Healthy eating** units.)

11 Tell the children that sometimes the trees in our parks are badly treated by very silly people. Ask them to write a notice, perhaps by a drawing of some kind, that could be placed near trees in the park warning people to look after the trees. This is an opportunity for creating a symbol for protecting trees. In groups, discuss what the notice will say and what the drawing might seek to show.

Music building block

Making musical instruments from discarded materials is an ideal way of introducing children to the concept of recycling waste-products.

MUSIC/TECHNOLOGY ACTIVITIES
C85 –86

1 Ask the children to bring from home or gather from around the school/class a collection of things that were once used for something but are no longer needed.

2 Ask the children to have a go at doing **copymaster 85 ((Making instruments)**. A line should be drawn from the home-made instrument to the circle that indicates how to make a musical sound. A different colour can be used for each category.

3 Using the materials collected, ask each child to make their own musical instrument. Make sure that there is a range of instruments that will enable a class 'orchestra' to be formed.

4 Once the instruments have been made and tried out for any modifications, form the orchestra and work on shaping up a familiar tune. The comb and papers should help to maintain the melody line.

● **Note** Instruments made from recycled waste are particularly good for creating sound effects and accompaniments to stories and poems.

5 Using **copymaster 86 (Making sounds)**, ask the class to describe the noises made from the waste materials shown.

6 Ask the children if they can think of other ways of using waste materials.

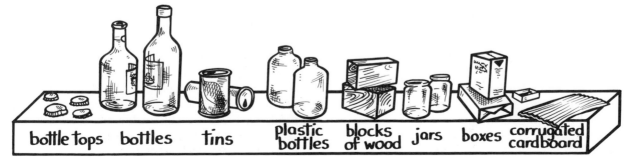

89

History building block

AT1 L2, 3
AT2 L3
AT3 L1, 2, 3

Knowledge and understanding of history at some point requires pupils to identify differences between past and present times, and this can be achieved through an examination and use of historical sources.

HISTORY ACTIVITIES

1 Ask the children where their water at home comes from.

2 Ask them if they have always been able to turn a tap on. Where else in the past might people have got their water for drinking?

3 Tell them that the village/town well was very important because it supplied all of the community with water for all of their needs. Tell the children that towns and villages were started by the sides of rivers to ensure that there was a fresh supply of water for the needs of people, animals and crops.

4 Undertake some local history research. Ask your library for any information on the history of where you live or a place near to you. Using maps, trace the nearest source of natural fresh water in the form of rivers, streams or lakes. Have the children draw simple maps, pictures of an early settlement and people dressed in the clothes of the period, by the source of water.

5 Together, consider how people long ago transported the water to where it was needed, either for cooking or for watering fields.

6 Ask the children what they need water for in their homes. Make a list of their ideas. Tell them that we need water to stay alive and that we could not live very long if we didn't have anything to drink at all.

7 Ask the children if they thought well water would be good for them. Do they think it would be clean or dirty water? What do they think might happen to them if they drank water from a well? Tell them that until water was cleansed and purified and delivered to our homes through pipes many people and especially children, died from illness caused by drinking 'dirty' water.

8 Ask the class if they know of any places or people in the world that have to rely on wells, streams or rivers for their drinking water today.

ASSESSMENT

Simply observing change over a period of time can count towards an assessment of learning.

1 Observe the class and individuals in the classroom/school environment: do they keep to the rules that they devised for helping to care for the environment?

2 What changes are apparent? What evidence is there for the changes? Are the children themselves aware of any changes in the environment? Ask them

- if they think it has improved
- if there is less litter
- are they washing their hands?
- are they using the litter bins?
- are they hanging their coats up?

3 Discuss with them how they think they could improve their immediate environment further.

4 Continue to observe individuals, groups and the class and use opportunities as they arise to reinforce learning.

5 Praise children who are seen to use the litter bins. These children, for example, might be identified by other children; reinforcing 'good behaviour' may be more effective in this instance than punishing 'inappropriate' behaviour.

6 A 'reward' system may be used that consists of stars or smiling faces on a class chart. If the children keep personal diaries of their achievements, suggest they record how they have helped to keep their environment safe and clean.

FEELING GOOD

Building blocks of the curriculum

Citizenship

- Helping others
- Valuing others
- Responsibility towards others

Art

- Painting and drawing as a way of expressing thoughts, moods and feelings
- Using work by artists to explore feelings

RE

- What it means to be part of the family
- The needs of those with disabilities

Environment

- How different environments affect moods, feelings, etc. (see Music and Geography)

History

- Comparing children's lives in the past with those of today in order to appreciate their own lives

Science

- Working in groups in order to investigate, explore and find out
- Taking responsibility – peer-led approaches

Music

- Using music to identify and express feelings

Geography

- Where we could go on holiday – mapwork; personal experience as a way of raising self-esteem

PE

- Physical exercise as a way to help us feel good
- Making up team games; learning from our peers

Mathematics

- Probability, random events: what one can do, can't do but might be able to do; what is impossible

English

- Self-reflection; what friends are
- Self-concept
- Speaking and listening

INTRODUCTION

Being healthy is more than just an absence of physical illness or disease. Holistic views of what constitutes good health usually include the mental, emotional and spiritual, as well as the physical aspects. Much of what we perceive as good mental or psychological health relates to how we see ourselves and to our self-concept. Rice (1990) comments that, 'self esteem seems to refer to how we feel about such personal aspects as appearances, abilities, behaviour, past experiences, and very importantly, the way others see us.... While self esteem and self concept relate to self descriptions, only self esteem contains an evaluative element'.

Hayes and Fors (1990) argue convincingly that an approach 'which increases self esteem through specific classroom learning activities and enhances student self esteem through personal involvement ... may be more likely to change health related behaviour for the better. People who feel good about themselves act more positively about their health because they feel they are worth it'.

Involving children and young people in their own learning is certainly one way of enhancing self-esteem. The evidence suggests that where children and young people learn from each other through the use of peer teaching approaches, the experience leads to positive gains in personal worth, achievement, self-confidence and self-esteem (Redman, 1988). In short, they feel good!

Curriculum Guidance 5 learning objectives

Pupils should:

- understand the importance of valuing oneself and others.
- begin to recognise the range of human emotions and ways to deal with these.
- begin to co-operate with others in work and play.

STARTING POINTS

- Give each child a copy of **copymaster 87 (I can do ...)** and ask them to think about each of the statements.

- Arrange the class in a large circle and ask each child to respond to the prompts (three times around the circle):

    Something I can do by myself is ....
    Something I can do *with* other children is ....
    Something I enjoy doing *for* other people is ......

    If a child cannot immediately think of something to say go back to them on completion of the round.

- Ask the children how they 'feel inside' when they do these things. Record their feelings on a large sheet of paper for all to see.

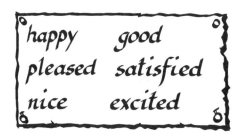

happy   good
pleased   satisfied
nice   excited

- Give each child a copy of **copymaster 88 (Feeling good inside)** and ask them to draw a picture of themselves when they are 'feeling good inside'.

- Suggest that if they are feeling good inside then their picture will be a happy one – ask them how they could show that.

- Suggest that the children now write down a short list of the things that they can do by themselves, etc. as suggested on **copymaster 87**.

- Mount and display their pictures and writing around the classroom.

Kevin   Debbie

Tony   things I can do
            things I enjoy
            things I can

Class 2. Feeling Good

- Tell the children that the following lessons are all about feeling good about ourselves.

English building block

| AT1 L1, 2, 3 |
| AT2 L1, 2, 3 |
| AT3 L1, 2, 3 |
| AT4 L1, 2, 3 |
| AT5 L1, 2, 3 |

Self-reflection is an important part of the development of self-concept and as a skill needs practice in a supportive atmosphere.

ENGLISH ACTIVITIES

C89

1 Ask the children what qualities or special things they look for in a friend. Record these on a large sheet of paper or on the board.

> my friend is ------
>
> nice to me
> buys presents
> has me to tea
> doesn't fight me
> shares things

2 Now ask the children what they think are the nice things about themselves. Ask every child in the class if possible or do it in the round.

3 Ask them what they think are the 'not so nice things' about themselves. Ask them individually or as volunteers to say how they think they could be better. Record these on a large sheet of paper or on the board.

4 Form the class into pairs. Ensure that every child has a partner and be sensitive to those who are 'isolates' in the class. If possible arrange the class so that boys and girls work with each other rather than with their best friends.

5 Invite the children, in turn, to describe their best friend. Can their partner guess who it is? (Tell them it doesn't have to be a person in the class – it could be an adult or a pet for example.)

6 In 'tables' or small groups (no more than four) each child, using copymaster should write a sentence about each other person sitting at their table or within their group. Tell them they can only write something nice about them:

> Mumtaz is nice because ....

7 When every child has completed their sentences, they should cut them out and given them to the child the sentence refers to. Each person should stick 'their sentences' on to a piece of paper or card and these should be displayed in the classroom. (Don't forget children who are absent!)

> how we could be better
>
> not be nasty
> share things
> help people
> listen to eachother

Geography building block

| AT1 L2, 3 |
| AT2 L1, 2, 3 |
| AT3 L2, 3 |
| AT4 L1, 2, 3 |
| AT5 L1, 2, 3 |

Valuing personal experience is a good way of raising self-esteem and helping children to feel good about themselves.

GEOGRAPHY ACTIVITIES

C90

Where would I like to go on holiday---- Florida
Tenby
India
Poole
Wales

1 Ask the children where they might like to go on holiday this year. Record their destinations on a large sheet of paper, using simple atlases or large class maps of the UK, Europe, world; look these up together. If you have a large map of the world, each child could make a personal flag to mark their destination.

2 Ask the children to bring in a photograph of themselves and their family on holiday or an outing which shows them having fun.

3 Invite each child to hold up the photograph for the class to see and ask them to tell everyone where it was and what they were doing. As each child does this mount their photographs on to a very large sheet of paper, writing underneath the name of the child and the holiday/outing location.

You may wish to embellish the display with humorous comments.

4 Ask the children to describe what they did on their holiday/day out, what the good/exciting things were and how they 'felt inside'. What made them feel good? You may wish to do this as a class activity or have the children reflect in small groups and then report back to the whole class.

5 Using **copymaster 90 (Picture postcards)**, tell the children to write a postcard to their best friend describing their holiday or outing and why they are feeling good. In the space provided, have them draw and colour a picture of a special memory from their holiday/day out.

6 Mount all of their postcards and display them in the classroom.

Postcards from our holidays

Dear Anne

7 Suggest to the class that they will all agree to send a partner a postcard from their holiday/outing destination. Tell them to make sure they know that person's address!

It is important to consider that, because of family circumstances, some children do not go away on holiday, especially abroad. Embarrassment can be avoided by addressing where the children would like to go and by encouraging them to think of enjoyable outings with the family.

Art building block

Painting and drawing are often used as a way of expressing feelings and innermost thoughts. Colours are significant statements of mood, feelings and emotions.

ART ACTIVITIES

1. Provide each table with a book of paintings perhaps of well-known artists or examples of paintings by artists from across the world. Alternatively, the children may wish to bring in a print from home.

2. Ask the children to select paintings that could generally be described as 'sad', 'happy', 'exciting', 'lonely', 'scary', 'peaceful'. Discuss together what it is about the paintings that make people think that of them. Make a list of children's observations about paintings in each of the mentioned groups.

3. Having previously given out paints, brushes, etc., to each table, ask the children to suggest some colours which could be used for describing 'happy' feelings. Similarly, ask the children to suggest some colours which could be used for describing 'sad' feelings.

4. Show the picture of the 'Sunflowers' painted by Vincent Van Gogh. Discuss with the children whether they think this is a happy picture and, if so, why?

5. Differentiate between warm colours, cool colours and cold colours. You may wish to look at the colours of the spectrum (rainbow) or reinforce the nature of primary and secondary colours.

6. Tell the children to paint a happy picture of their own using only warm, happy colours. Remind them of the painting of the 'Sunflowers' by Van Gogh.

7. Display the pictures around the classroom with appropriate titles.

8. Suggest to the children that they think of warm, happy colours whenever they are feeling sad or unhappy.

PE building block

Physical exercise helps us to feel good besides keeping us in good shape – 'looking good, feeling good!' Children can invent their own games, plan and demonstrate them to the class.

PE ACTIVITIES

1. Divide the class into mixed groups using a fun activity.

2. Tell each group that they have got to think of some new games for the rest of the class to play, which can involve them in running, jumping, throwing and catching balls, etc.

3. Inform the children that they should think very carefully about any rules that would help the game/activity to work well and how they are going to teach the rest of the class.

4. When the groups are ready ask each in turn to demonstrate their new game/activity to the remainder of the class. Then ask the group to help the class to 'do' the game/activity. (They will need to explain its purpose, rules and procedures.)

Intervene if you feel that the game/activity is not safe, if you believe that not all of the children are participating, if the children need help in making decisions or implementing any rules or if the game/activity is not 'fair' in any sense. If you intervene, make sure the children understand why.

5. When every group has had a turn ask each group how they felt when they demonstrated their game/activity and if they thought that it had been successful.

6. To consolidate, ask the children to complete **copymaster 91 (Our game)**. How do they think the games or activities could be improved?

95

Mathematics building block

AT5 L1, 2, 3

Recognising that there are possible outcomes of simple random events and that while there is a degree of certainty and uncertainty for some events, there are certain events that are impossible. This falls within the category of 'probability' in Mathematics.

In knowing about ourselves it is important to realise what we can do, what we can't do but might be able to and what is simply impossible to do.

MATHEMATICS ACTIVITIES

C92

1 Discuss with the children that there are certain things that we know will happen, certain things that we are not sure about and some things that we know are impossible. Illustrate this by placing the children in pairs and issue a coin to each pair.

2 Ask the children to toss the coin and to write/say the following:

When I toss a coin it is certain that ....
When I toss a coin it is uncertain that ....
When I toss a coin it is impossible that ....

3 Similarly, rolling a die ask the children to write/say the following:

When I roll a die it is certain that ....
When I roll a die it might happen that ....
When I roll a die it can't happen that ....

4 Using **copymaster 92 (Little boxes)**, ask the children to write in the first box something they know they can do; in the second box something they can't do but would like to, and in the third box something they know is impossible for them to do.

5 Arrange three boxes appropriately labelled and placed in the classroom. When the children have written their statements ask them to put them in the correct boxes.

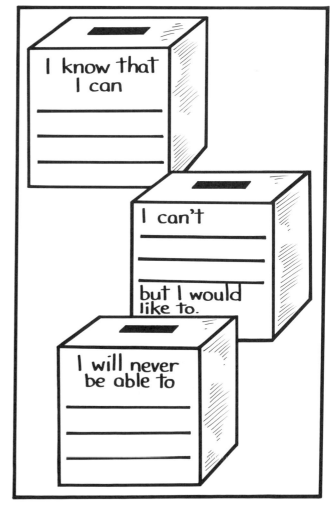

6 Open the boxes and (a) categorise the answers; (b) discuss the answers within the context of what we can do, can't but would like to (how might this be achieved?) and things that are impossible for us to do (or are they really?)

96

Science building block

> AT1 L1, 2, 3

Science is often a group activity involving children working together exploring, investigating, discovering and talking about what they see and find out. Within the context of psychological health the essential activity is to consider the individual responsibility towards the group and the group's responsibility towards the class.

SCIENCE ACTIVITIES

1 Prepare a range of group Science activities pitched at the level at which the children are, involving some or all of the following: research, experimentation, observation, classification and recording.

2 Arrange the children into working groups of four, five or six.

3 Make the aim of the exercise perfectly clear; namely that they are going to complete their given/chosen activity and then they are going to tell the class what they have learned, and how they went about the task they were given. In short, they are to become the teachers and will have to answer questions the others in the class ask them.

4 When each group has made a presentation hand out copies of **copymaster 93 (Teaching the class)** and discuss the following points.

1) How did it feel to work in a group?
2) Who felt they had the most important part?
3) Did everyone feel as if they were part of a team?
4) Did anyone feel left out?
5) Did anyone feel that they, or anyone else, was the leader?
6) Did the group have any problems? If so, what did they do about them?
7) How did it feel being the teacher and teaching the others in the class?
8) How did it feel being taught by someone other than the teacher?
9) What makes a good teacher?

5 Discuss with the children what is important about working in a group. On a board or large sheet of paper, write the statements the children make and then display the answers in the classroom (e.g. working in a group means … taking turns, not shouting, not being bossy).

RE building block

What it means to be part of a family is an important part of this book (see **Families**). Caring schools often have a 'family ethos' and see all who work and learn within them as part of an extended family, but does this embrace extend as far as children with physical or mental disability?

RE ACTIVITIES

1 Ask the children what they would most miss if they were no longer able to come to school. Write down the children's answers on a board or large piece of paper.

2 Are there any children who are unable to come to school? Why might that be?

3 Focus with the class on those children who are generally unable to come to school because of physical or mental disability. Consider what happens to those children. (An excellent series that informs children in a positive and sensitive way about children with handicaps is *One Day at a Time* by Thomas Bergman, published by Gareth Stevens Children's Books, 31 Newingham Green, London N16 9PU.)

4 Working in groups, ask each group to think about one particular disability from the following: deafness, blindness, mental disability, immobility/confined to a wheelchair. Ask each group to think about the problems that a handicapped child joining the class might be faced with and how the problem might be overcome.

5 If the class had a child with a disability coming to join it what difference would it make to the class? How would you make such a person welcome? Write a letter or draw a picture telling/showing them how you are going to help them.

Susan James
Class 7
Westmount
Primary School

Dear Adrian,

I am very much looking forward to you coming - - - - -

6 Tell the children the story of 'The Happy Prince' by Oscar Wilde, or stories concerning Jesus healing the sick and children in particular (Matthew 8, 9 and 10).

7 Invite the children to say why it would be good to have children with a handicap as members of the class family. What sort of person would they have to be? Write down the children's suggestions on a board or large sheet of paper.

History building block

AT1 L2, 3
AT2 L3
AT3 L1, 2, 3

One way for children to appreciate the worth of their self-esteem is for them to view themselves in relation to others. This can sometimes be achieved by comparing what they have in terms of relative comforts, supportive families and general care with those of other children past and present.

HISTORY ACTIVITIES

C94 –95

1 Suggest to the children that they could no longer come to school but instead will have to go out to work. Ask each child what they think they could do to earn a living. Write any suggestions on a board or large sheet of paper.

2 Explain to the class that a long time ago children as young as four had to work because their family was too poor to feed them. Ask the children to look at pictures from different sources.

3 Some children worked down mines either opening trap doors, pushing trucks or carrying baskets of coal. Tell the children that the working day was usually from early morning until evening. Using **copymaster 94 (Working children)**, ask each child to follow the journey of Peggy, who is eight years old, as she carries coal from the coal face to the truck in the mine. Where there is a box, that is where they can step in and help her by doing something to make her feel better. Ask them to write or draw a picture of what you would do.

4 On the board or large sheet of paper, draw a central line forming two columns headed:

A day in Peggy's life	A day in our life

5 Underneath each heading ask children to compare the difference between their life and Peggy's. Consider how Peggy might feel while she works, how she might feel at the end of the day, what goes through her mind while she works, what she eats and what if she wanted to use the toilet? What does she do when she goes home after work?

6 Using **copymaster 95 (Now and then)**, ask the children to draw a picture showing themselves at 'work' at school or at home, and one of Peggy at work down the mine.

Music building block

Music can arouse a variety of feelings affecting the listener. Although there is often general agreement over which pieces fall into specific categories, it is down to the listener to decide what effect the music has on him or her.

MUSIC ACTIVITIES

1 Invite the children to bring into school music that makes them either happy or sad. Play the music and ask the person who brought the music to say to the others why they have chosen it.

2 On the board write the four categories:

- sad
- lonely
- angry
- frightened.

3 Using **copymaster 96 (Musical feelings)**, play the children four pieces of pre-selected music and ask them to place a number in the box at the corner of the appropriate picture. Discuss the results and why it was that children thought that each piece of music belonged in the box in which they placed it.

4 Ask the children to think of people having the feelings shown in each section on the copymaster. Ask the children to say what they could do make a sad/lonely/angry/frightened person feel better.

5 Reproduce the copymaster on a large scale and place the answers given by each child into the appropriate section.

sad	lonely	angry	frightened
* be their friend * hold their hand	* play with them * sit next to them	* make them laugh * tickle them * tell a joke	* hug them * smile at them

99

ASSESSMENT

If the notion of self-esteem relates to self-description and contains an evaluative element, then only the individual can do this effectively.

1 Give each child in the class circles of self-adhesive paper in different colours (red, orange, yellow, green, purple, blue).

2 Ask them to sort them into warm/happy colours, cool/sad colours.

3 Tell the children to go through their various class-work books and decide what colour circle they should give each piece according to how well they felt they had done and if they were pleased with the results.

4 Tell them that anything they were pleased with or had worked hard on should be given a 'warm' colour, while they should give 'cool' colours to areas they need to work harder at and improve.

5 When they have done this, using a template to draw round, ask them to draw a large circle at the end of their work and write in it.

This can be coloured in the appropriate colour.

6 You may wish to discuss with individual children their choice of 'feeling colours' and where possible to encourage them (if appropriate) to change the colour stickers or larger circle to a warm colour.

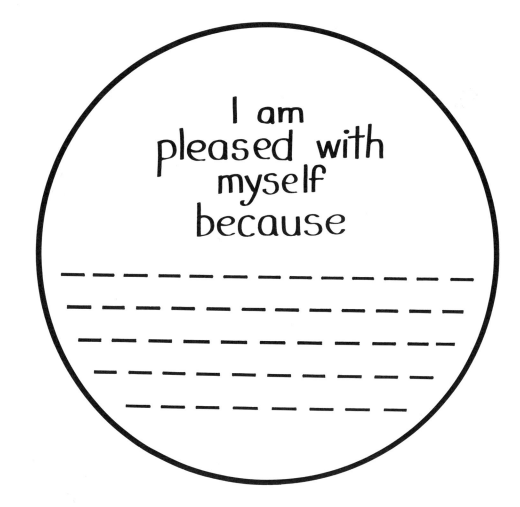

RECOMMENDED READING FOR CHILDREN

Medicines and drugs
Dr Sean, P. Breinburg, Bodley Head.
Miss Dose the Doctor's Daughter, A. Ahlberg, Puffin.
Going to the Doctor, C. Jessel, Methuen.
Topsy and Tim (Series), J. Adamson, Blackie.
    Go to the Hospital
    Go to the Doctors
    Get their Eyes Tested
    Meet the Dentist

Growing up
Lucy and Tom Go to School, S. Hughes, Bodley Head.
My Big Brother, P. Gili, Hodder & Stoughton.
Starting School, A. Ahlberg, Viking Kestrel.
You'll Soon Grow Into Them, Tich, P. Hutchins, Picture Puffin.
Tich, P. Hutchins, Picture Puffin.
The Dream Beast, J. Richardson, Red Fox.
How a Baby is Made, P. Knudson, Piccolo Books.
Where Did I Come From?, P. Mayle, Macmillan.

Families
Can I Help Dad?, S. Grindley, Simon & Schuster.
Amber's other Grandparents, P. Bonnici, Bodley Head.
Granpa, J. Burningham, Red Fox.
Why Did Grandma Die?, T. Madler, Blackwell.
I'll Always Love You, H. Wilhelm, Picture Knight.
Dad's Back, J. Ormerod, Walker Books.
Mum's Home, J. Ormerod, Walker Books.
Dear Daddy, P. Depasquier, Anderson Books.
Dogger, S. Hughes, Bodley Head/Lion.

Being safe
Rosie's Walk, P. Hutchins, Bodley Head/Puffin
Topsy and Tim Safety Book, J. Adamson, Blackie.
Not Now, Bernard, D. McKee, Anderson/Sparrow.
I'm Going to Get You, T. Ross, Anderson Press.

Exercising
Topsy and Tim Go Swimming, J. Adamson, Blackie.
Topsy and Tim in the Gym, J. Adamson, Blackie.
Mr Mens' Sports Day, R. Hargreaves, Stern.
Mr Lazy, R. Hargreaves, Stern.

Healthy eating
Don't Forget the Bacon, P. Hutchins, Bodley Head/Puffin.
The Door Bell Rang, P. Hutchins, Picture Puffin.
The Very Hungry Caterpillar, E. Carle, Puffin.
The Baked Bean Queen, R. Impney, Picture Puffin.
The Tiger Who came to Tea, J. Kerr, Collins.
The Magic Pasta Pot, T. De Paola, Anderson/Beaver.
The Teddy Bears Go Shopping, S. Gretz, Hippo.

Keeping clean
Time to Get Out of the Bath, Shirley, J. Burningham, Picture Lions.
Doing the Washing, S. Garland, Bodley Head/Puffin.
The King's Toothache, C. West, Walker Books.
The Tale of Mucky Mabel, J. Willis, Sparrow.
Andrew's Bath, D. McPhail, Blackie.
The Beast in the Bath Tub, K. Stevens, Marks & Spencer.
I Want My Potty, T. Ross, Anderson Press.
Measles and Sneezles, J. Curry, Red Fox.

The environment
In My Garden, R. Maris, Walker Books.
Days With Frog and Toad (Series), A. Lobel, Puffin.
Ming Mo Loves the Mountain, A. Lobel, McCrae.
Teddy Bears Went to the Seaside, S. Gretz, Hippo.
Dear Zoo, Campbell, Picture Puffin.
Mr Mataxmas One Man Band, S. Moxley, Hodder & Stoughton.

Feeling good
We Are Best Friends, Aliki, Bodley Head.
Feelings, Aliki, Bodley Head.
The Bad Tempered Ladybird, E. Carle, Puffin.
Little Red Hen, M. Zemach, Picture Puffin.
Let's Be Friends Again, H. Wilhelm, Picture Knight.

Other useful resources
Blueprints Topics, J. Fitzsimmons and R. Whiteford, Stanley Thornes 1990.
Blueprints Science 5–7 Teacher's Resource Book and Pupil's Copymasters, J. Fitzsimmons and R. Whiteford, Stanley Thornes 1991.

Skills for the Primary School Child (SPSC), A. Moon, TACADE 1990.

Streets Ahead, Modules 1–4, S. Aucott, ROSPA in association with Spar 1990.

Health for Life (1 & 2), T. Williams, N. Wetton and A. Moon, HEA/Nelson 1989.

Happy Heart (1 & 2), M. Sleap and P. Warburton, HEA/Nelson 1990.

Time To Dance (plus cassette tape), M. Ware, Belaire Publications 1987.

Gym Joey BAGA. For use with BAGA Pre school Gymnastics and Movement Programme.

Fit For Life Level 1, Health Education For Slow Learners, HEA/Macmillan 1986.

Heading for Health, Birmingham Schools' Health Education Policy, Birmingham LEA Health Education Unit 1990.

REFERENCES

Introduction

Science in the National Curriculum, DES and Welsh Office, London HMSO 1989.

Science for Ages 5 to 16: Proposals of the Secretary of State for Education and Science and the Secretary of State for Wales, London HMSO 1991.

'Health Education and the National Curriculum', J. Donahue, *Journal of the Institute of Health Education* Vol. 29 No. 2 1991.

Resolution of the Ministers of Education meeting in Council 23 November 1988 concerning Health Education in Schools.

Official Journal of the European Communities No. C3/1, Brussels 1989.

Health Education from 5 to 16 Curriculum Matters 6, HMI London HMSO 1986.

Personal and Social Education from 5 to 16 Curriculum Matters 14, London HMSO 1989.

Personal and Social Education in the National Curriculum, J. Lloyd in *Skills for the Primary School Child: The Manual*, A. Moon, TACADE 1990.

'Non Smokers Do it Without Coughing', J. Lloyd, *Health Education Journal* Vol. 50 No. 1 1991.

The Whole Curriculum, Guidance 3. National Curriculum Council, York 1990a.

Health Education, Curriculum Guidance 5. National Curriculum Council, York 1990b.

Health Education, Ministry of Education, Pamphlet 31, London HMSO 1956.

A Picture of Health: What do you do that makes you healthy and keeps you healthy?, T. Williams, N. Wetton and A. Moon, London HEA 1989.

Medicines and drugs

'What do children know?', J. Lloyd and G. Combes, *Health Education Journal* Vol. 47 1988. *A Picture of Health: What do you do that makes you healthy and keeps you healthy?* T. Williams, N. Wetton and A. Moon, London HEA 1989.

Growing up

Health Education from 5 to 16, Curriculum Matters 6, HMI London HMSO 1986.

Science in the National Curriculum, DES and Welsh Office, London HMSO 1989.

Families

The Needs of Parents – Practice and Policy in Parent Eduction, G. Pugh and E. De'Ath, National Children's Bureau Series, Macmillan 1984.

Conscious Choices: The Goal of Family Life Education, K. Torkington in *Family Lifestyles*, D. Braun and N. Eisenstadt, OUP 1985.

Health Education, Curriculum Guidance 5. National Curriculum Council, York 1990.

Being safe

Streets Ahead Modules 1–4, Sue Aucott, ROSPA in Association with Spar 1990.

Exercising

'Children are fit but not active', *Education and Health* Vol. 7 No. 2 1990, pp. 28–32.

The Syllabus of Physical Exercises for Schools, The Board of Education, London HMSO 1909.

'The Changing Face of Physical Education', F. Dowling, *Health Education Journal* Vol. 45 No. 1 1986.

'Health and Fitness in the Physical Education Curriculum: Regression or Progress?', A. Williams, *Health Education Journal* Vol. 46 No. 3 1987.

UK Levels of Health First Report June 1991, Faculty of Public Health and Medicine, Royal College of Physicians 1991.

Healthy eating

Nutrition Guidelines in Britain: A Discussion Paper, National Advisory Committee on Nutrition Education, Health Education Council 1983.

Medical Aspects of Food Policy, Diet and Cardiovascular Disease, Committee on Medical Aspects of Food Policy DHSS 1984.

Don't Break Your Heart – All you need to know about your heart, B. Lynch BBC TV, Sidgwick and Jackson, London 1987

The environment

Environmental Education: Curriculum Guidance No 7, National Curriculum Council, York 1990.

Feeling good

'Peer Teaching in Health Education. A Study into the Potential of Young People as Educators in Schools' J. Redman (Unpublished MSc Dissertation), University of Hull 1988.

'Self Esteem and Health Instruction, Challenges for Curriculum Development' D.M. Hayes and S.W. Fors, *Journal of School Health* Vol. 60 No. 5 1990.

Promoting Self Esteem in School, W. Rice in *Skills for the Primary School Child: The Manual*, A. Moon, TACADE 1990.